Romeyn de Hooghe the etcher

Mr ROMEIN DE HOOGHE.

QUOS ALIT ARTES.

H. Bos *Pinx*. J. Houbraken *Sculps. 1733*.

Romeyn de Hooghe the etcher

contemporary portrayal of Europe 1662-1707

by John Landwehr

A. W. Sijthoff-Leiden

Oceana-Dobbs Ferry N.Y.

MCMLXXIII

ISBN 90 286 0332 8 (Sijthoff)
ISBN 379-00011-3 (Oceana)
Library of Congress Catalog Card Number: 72-92918
© A. W. Sijthoff International Publishing Company, N.V. 1973
Printed in the Netherlands.

BY THE SAME AUTHOR:

Dutch Emblem Books. A Bibliography. Utrecht 1962. *Bibliotheca Emblematica* I.

Fable-Books in the Low Countries. A concise bibliography until 1800. Nieuwkoop 1963.

Emblem Books in the Low Countries 1554-1949. A Bibliography. Utrecht 1970. *Bibliotheca Emblematica* III.

Romeyn de Hooghe as Book Illustrator 1645-1708. A Bibliography. Amsterdam, New York 1970.

Splendid Ceremonies. State Entries and Royal Funerals in the Low Countries, 1515-1791. Nieuwkoop, Leiden 1971.

German Emblem Books 1531-1888. A Bibliography. Utrecht 1972. *Bibliotheca Emblematica* V.

voor Roger

CONTENTS

Although prints by De Hooghe have been the object of some research, until the present there has been no comprehensive monograph on his separately published prints: it has been the opinion of art historians, print collectors and antiquarian booksellers that De Hooghe's oeuvre is too extensive to be catalogued. A. von Wurzbach made this statement in 1906:

"...Eine Aufzählung der Blätter de Hooghe's wäre eine dankbare Aufgabe für eine Monographie. In der Versteigerung Cayeux, 1769, wurde ein Werk bestehend aus 570 Blätter verkauft. Die Albertina in Wien besitzt drei grosse Foliobände, welche noch weit mehr Blätter enthalten.[1] Sie sind für die Zeitgeschichte von höchsten Interesse und es ist nur zu bedauern, dass sich noch keiner der holländischen Forscher dieser dankbaren[2] und wichtigen Aufgabe unterzogen hat..."

More recently Mr. Georg Rósza wrote this:

"...Nachdem 1906 bereits A. von Wurzbach darüber klagte, dass de Hooghe's umfangreiches Oeuvre bisher noch nicht zur Aufarbeitung gelangt war, stellte 1924 auch M. D. Henkels im Thieme-Becker Lexikon veröffentlichter Artikel über de Hooghe fest, dass eine kritische Zusammenfassung aller auf die ausserholländische europäische Zeitgeschichte bezüglichen Werke des Künstlers noch ausständig sei. Diese Behauptung besteht auch heute noch zurecht, zumal in dieser Hinsicht auch im neuesten umfangreichen Katalog von F. W. H. Hollstein über die Arbeiten der holländischen Holzschneider, Kupferstecher und Radierer noch gewisse Lücken[3] klaffen..."
Romeyn de Hooghe und die Türkenkriege in Ungarn. *Oua Holland 1962 p. 102.*

Now in this monograph I have attempted to earmark the material arranging it in a certain order. This survey I trust may give the user easier access to the phantastic Baroque world of De Hooghe: his early prints on rustic scenes, journalistic prints, political caricatures, portraits, topographical etchings and those on morals and customs.

De Hooghe left us also some books of which *Spiegel van Staat,*[4] 1706-1707, is the most interesting one in that it discloses on many occasions the etcher's outlook on his time, his surroundings and his fellowman; I selected a few pages to be translated into English which are printed opposite the original version. From these pages I selected some sentences which nicely illustrate some topographical and other prints.

1. In addition five folio volumes from the Collection of Prince Eugene of Savoye-sign. HB LXXI, 1-5.- which contain thousands of book illustrations and many prints separately published.
2. I expect that this survey may induce some more students to write articles and books on De Hooghe.
3. I added over 100 prints, not counting later states.
4. *Mirror of State of the United Netherlands.*

ACKNOWLEDGEMENTS:

I should like to thank Mr. and Mrs. J. G. Jones for their expert translation of the introductory pages to *Spiegel van Staat*.
I am equally indebted to Miss W. A. H. Crol, curator of *Stichting Atlas van Stolk* at Rotterdam and her assistant Miss M. E. Deelen, who tremendously simplified my task of gathering the basic material for the Section Newsprints.

With the same vigour I should like to thank photographers J. M. Baris, Rotterdam, G. Th. Delamarre, Bunnik and Staff members[1] of:

Amsterdam: Gemeente Archief, Rijksmuseum and Universiteits Bibliotheek.
Breda: Gemeente Archief, Kasteel and Museum.
Brussels: Koninklijke Bibliotheek.
Delft: Gemeente Archief.
Haarlem: Gemeente Archief and Teyler Museum.
Hoorn: Archief and Museum.
The Hague: Algemeen Rijksarchief, Koninklijke Bibliotheek, Museum Meermanno-Westreenianum and Rijksbureau voor Kunsthistorische Documentatie.
Leyden: Hoogheemraadschap Rijnland, Prentenkabinet, Universiteits Bibliotheek.

Rotterdam: Gemeente Archief and Boymans-van Beuningen Museum.
Utrecht: De Balye van de Duitsche Orde.
Vienna: Albertina.
New York: The New York Public Library.[2]
Boston: Museum of Fine Arts.
London: The Printroom of the British Museum.

This catalogue could not have been completed[3] without the splendid co-operation of aforementioned Institutions.

"I have done this work for my own pleasure on festival days and without being engaged by more important matters. Who feels so inclined can read this in the same way or leave it if he has more useful or necessary things to do…"

Voorschoten, Summer 1972

1. The bulk of the illustrations is reproduced for the first time.
2. Unfortunately the Metropolitan Museum of Arts was closed on the day I was in New York City.
3. I aimed at a complete catalogue indeed, but its use will show what is missing.

13

INTRODUCTORY NOTES

Romeyn de Hooghe was born in 1645. He was a nephew of the well-known painter Pieter de Hoogh(e)[1]. On his background and life only very little is known.

Our artist has had thorough schooling: his educational background finds expression in his political treatises such as *Schouburgh der Nederlandse Veranderingen* (1674) and *Esopus in Europa* (1701), as well as in his politico-juridical *Spiegel van Staat* (1706-1707) and his scholarly *Hieroglyphica* which found a publisher almost three decades after his death (1735). His versatile artistic talent is also apparent from the sculptures[2], paintings and an ornamental, etched, goblet[3]. De Hooghe's etchings were to some extent done on order of publishers[4] and influential people. His early work (1662) consists of some etchings of rustic scenes after Nicolaes Berchem, while a few – such as the *Feast of the solstice* – are of his own invention. De Hooghe's first Newsprints seem to be Admiral de Ruyter's exploits near Rochester and Chatham (1667) after W. Schellink's design and two versions of the Peace conference and Ratification between England and the Republic at Breda (1667). In 1668 he stayed at Paris where he etched the Baptism of the Dauphin "dessigné sur les lieux", but it is not until 1672 that De Hooghe really became involved in reporting on European wars, the year when Louis XIV with the Elector of Cologne and the Bishop of Munster invaded and attacked the Republic.

De Hooghe had reviewed or rather etched some political developments in *Hollandsche Mercurius* since 1670 and the etcher's cooperation with publisher Pieter Casteleyn lasted until 1691, when this Newspaper was taken over by an Amsterdam publisher. Ever since Willem III was sworn in Commander-in-chief over the Forces in the Republic (1672) De Hooghe has etched the memorable feats performed by Willem III not only in *Mercurius Print, Princelycke Almanach* (1674, 1675, 1676, 1677, 1680), *Orangien Wonderspiegel* (1675) but also in prints illustrating the *Glorious Revolution* and many others. A. F. van der Meulen painted the victories of King Louis XIV, De Hooghe rendered in etchings his services to King Willem III, who in recognition appointed him commissary and supervisor of the mining district of Lingen. However the allegation of Mr. G. van Rijn cannot be upheld that De Hooghe was a "slavish follower of his King": his prints on the assault and murder of Cornelis and Johan de Witt

1. See *De Wapenheraut* XXIV, 1920: pages 213-216.
2. See his drawings for statues for Het Loo, pages 356 *ff.*
3. Which is on show in Rijnlandshuis of Hoogheemraadschap, Leyden.
4. Nicolaus Visscher, Pieter Persoy in Amsterdam and J. Tangena in Leyden to mention the most important ones.
5. Illustrated by Jan Harrewijn.

bear rather witness of an independant mind. Another hero in the Republic was John Sobieski on whose life and exploits C. van der Linde published a biography which appeared in Amsterdam 1675[5] (a year after he was crowned King of Poland in Cracow). De Hooghe made a portrait of and several large etchings on John III of Poland, the last being an apotheosis of the Polish King in 1685 (in four leaves!). As a mark of recognition he was raised to the peerage of Poland. Would Franciscus Mollo (Mello?) whose nuptial (1674) he etched, have promoted this? When reviewing De Hooghe's journalistic prints we find that his separately published prints can be labelled all *Newsprints* but one i.e. the *Siege and Relief of Leyden* (1572/4), which exception confirms the rule. Some twenty plates have been retouched and adapted for subsequent events. It is difficult to say in which cases the adapted plates are still by the hand of De Hooghe, who died in 1708. One may be certain though that the nearer the Republic the war scenes were depicted, the more accurate are his etchings; on the other hand those depicting the wars against the Swedish, the French, the Turks and the Hungarians may sometimes lack in accuracy, they certainly reflect the cultural climate in which this European etcher of the late seventeenth century lived. With the *Roi Soleil* in France and Willem III in the Republic the fashion for the spectacular and the allegoric passed all bounds. The increased splendour can be estimated from merely glancing at some prints by De Hooghe: The ceremonies and fire-works at Breda (1667), The baptism of the Dauphin (1668), Peace negociated between England and the Republic with fire-works in The Hague (1674), Coronation of John III in Cracow (1674), Allegories on the feats of Willem III (1674 etc.), Funeral of Amalia van Solms (1675), Funeral of P. Wirtz (1676), Funeral of Admiral de Ruyter (1677), The marriage of Willem III and Mary Stuart (1677), Glorification of John III of Poland (1685), The glorious entry of Leopold I of Austria into Brussels (1686) etc. etc.

These instances can give an idea of his whole production, which consists of etchings depicting funeral pomps of eminent persons, solemn entrances, illuminations, battles and sieges, the horrors of war, floods, allegories, armorial bearings, castles and parks of eminent people, mausoleums, portraits of V.I.P.'s, political caricatures and so on. Some of the etcher's opinions are expressed on the next pages.

SPIEGEL van STAAT

DES

VEREENIGDE NEDERLANDS.

Waar in

De Macht en 't Vry Beftier,

Van yder der Zeven Verbonde PROVINCIEN en haar
byzondere Steeden,

Zo in Rechten als Regeeringen werd ontvouwd.

Aanwyzende

Aan, de In, en Uytheemschen, alle de Hooge en Lage Rechtbanken, Collegien en Ampten, dewelke in de zelve, tot
dienst van den Staat, en het Recht, zyn ingesteld.

Hoe, wanneer en waar, voor de zelve yets te verrichten is.

DOOR

Mr: ROMYN DE HOOGHE.

EERSTE DEEL:

t'AMSTERDAM,

By JAN TEN HOORN, Boekverkooper 1706.

17

PREFACE

Passing by our own affairs without noticing, knowing about foreign ones, a mole at home, an eagle outside, makes idle pomp but causes damage to prosperity. It is a failing common to most people; what we could know daily we rarely know. How grandiloquently a traveller or reader reels off the details of the republics of the *Venetians,* the *Genoeses* or the *Swiss,* how neatly somebody talks about the State-meeting at *Regensburg,* about the structure of the Electoral and High Royal Members there with the free towns? And how embarrassed is the same pedant when it comes to the reigning Members of his own country. The election of a Speaker in *England,* the rights of cities and strongholds to send their representatives to the House of Commons one knows it here; and one can name the Nobility of the Realm, Bishops and persons of the High Classes who sit in the House of Lords. But if one asks the same person who are the Knighthood and Nobility of *Holland* and her allies he will hesitate. What could be more for our good than the necessary knowledge of such affairs which serve body and soul? In this blessed time, besides knowing of God's being and His sanctifying mercy, some occupation with our statecraft is becoming. After the Holy Lessons we should recommend to youth the study of our free government and the grounds on which it had been exercised.

For how can a Commonwealth exist but by a moral obedience of the people? How can the gentlemen chosen to govern proceed with sure steps to maintain general and particular laws, privileges or freedoms unless the leader and the led each knows for himself his duty and limitation. To govern ambitiously or self-interestedly comes from wicked men; being slack, negligent, pusillanimous in those matters from ignorant people; being contradictious, obstinate and recalcitrant amongst the burghers or countrymen

VOOR-REEDEN.

Nze eygene zaken zonder opmerking voorby te gaan, vreemde te kennen, 't Huys een Mol, buyten een Arend te zyn, maakt ydele praal in de ommegang, maar schade in de welvaart. 't Is een gebrek, den meesten gemeen; 't geen wy dagelyks konnen weten, weten wy zelden. Hoe wydlustig, gaat een Reyziger of Lezer van grond, in de byzonderheden van de Gemeene besten, der *Venetianen, Genuëzen,* of *Zwitzers,* hoe net reedeneerd yemand van de Ryksvergadering te *Regensburg,* van de zamenstel van de Keur en Hoog Vorstelyke Leden aldaar met de Vrysteden? en hoe verlegen is de zelve betweter, zo hy op de heerschende Leden van zyn eygen Landschap komt; De verkiezing in *Engeland* van een Spreker, de rechten der Steden en Burgten, om de haren te zenden in 't Lagerhuys weetmen hier: en men kan optellen, de Ryks Baroenen, Bisschoppen en hoge Stands perzonen, welke zitting in het Hoger Huys hebben, maar zo men die zelve vraagt, welke de Ridderschap en Edelen van *Holland* of zyne Bondgenooten zyn, hy zal twyfelen. Wat kan ons tot nut komen, als de noodzakelyke kennis van zulke zaken, die de ziel, en 't lyf dienst doen? by de gezegende tyd, van Gods wezen, en zyn zaligmakende genade te kennen, voegt wel, eenige beezigheyd van onze Staatkunde. Wy behoren na de Heylige Lessen, de Vorm van Ons Vry bestier, hoe en op welke gronden die gevest is, nevens de manieren op de welke die geoeffend werd, de jeugd aan te beveelen.

Want hoe kan een Gemeenebest bestaan, als door een zedige gehoorzaamheyd des Volks? hoe konnen de Heeren tot het bestier uytgekoren, met zekere treden toegaan, in het handhaven der gemeene of byzondere Wetten, Voorrechten of Vryheden, ten zy de bestierder, en bestierde, elk voor zyn Hoofd weet, zyn plicht en park. Wreevelmoedig, Heersch of Baatzuchtig de Regeering te voeren, komt van booze Mannen; slap, slof, laf, daar in te zyn van onkundige; Weerwoordig, Balstuyrig, weerspanfpannig onder de Borgers of Landluy te zyn, komt meeft van onkundige dwarspalen, die met een verkeerd begrip van vry-heyd, ongebonden willen zyn; windbuylen in 't kakelen, ver-quifters van 't hare, en luye ledigheyd voor groots leven hou-dende: deze zyn de werktuygen, om een Gemeene beft te be-derven ; met fnap van praal, op de naam van Geeft, en onder-houd van onryp nieuws, verkrygenfe by haar foort een naam, om de deugd en eerlykheyd, van hare Medeborgers, en 't ge-drag van hare wettige Overheden verdagt te maken; niewigheyd en quaad ftokende om onder een gemeen verderf, haar quade toe-ftand beft te dekken; of was 't mogelyk, alles in duygen te fmyten, en te azen van de vlyt en zuynigheyd der vromen. Om dat de goede Borgers niet zouden van zulken foort verleyd wer-den, luft my dit de doen drukken; ik heb daar op lang toege-legd, en onder vele beezigheden, fchoone middelen gehad, om yets tot myn oogwit te beryden, byna alle de Heeren der *Hol-landze* Steden, en haare Hoogfte Vergaderingen heb ik de eer gehad by tuffen tyden te dienen, alwaar ik middel had, om op te nemen en aan te tekenen, 't geen my diende, gelyk ik in myne reyzen alom buyten 's Lands reeds gedaan had: tuffen de binnenlandfe beezigheden, heb ik de Biffchoppen van *Osnabrug* en *Paderborn*, in hare oudheden te etzen, mogen zien : in *Bruf-fel* en *Antwerpen* vele werken doen maken, *Turnhout*, *Breda* en an-dere grensplaatzen moeten doorzien, en met de Commandery-en der *Duytze* Ridder ordre, de naafte Landfcheyding der Ver-eenigde Staat tegen *Duytfland*, konnen opmerken, gelyk den omtrek van *Zutphen*, *Overyffel* en *Drenth*, in het waarnemen van het Commiffarisfchap van *Lingen*, voor den Koning *William*; wiens groote gedachtenis eeuwen zal verduyren.

Ook verfchafte my het Hof op 't *Loo* te volgen, van eenige zaken, vry omftandiger naricht, wegens eenige onzer Provin-cien, van de welke men de Edelfte en Aanzienlykfte aldaar kon zien en fpreken. Deze voorbereydzelen, deden my een gebaan-de weg tot de uytvoering van myn toeleg verbeelden, en na dien ik, Borgers en Vreemden in verlegentheyd vond, wanneerze in of buyten *Holland*, erfenis aan te gaan, fchulden te innen, of ander belang waar te nemen hadden, behaagde 't my, ten dien-fte der In en Uytheemfe, de Rechtbanken, de Keuren en Wet-ten,

which comes mainly from ignorant, crossgrained fellows who – with the wrong idea of freedom – want to be unrestrained; wind-bags in a rattling vein, squandering their possessions and mistaking lazy idleness for high-life, these are the tools to ruin a commonwealth; with pretentious twaddle under the name of genius, and providing immature news, they obtain a name with their kind to fasten suspicion on the virtue and honesty of their fellow-citizens and the behaviour of their legal government; brewing innovation and mischief to cover up their vicious situation with general corruption; or if it were possible to destroy everything and to feed on the assiduity and thrift of the pious people. To prevent the good citizens to be tempted by such people I should like to have this printed. I have set myself to this for a long time, and amongst many occupations I had handsome resources to prepare something towards my intention, at times I have had the honour to serve almost all the gentlemen of the cities of Holland and their Highest Assemblies where I had the opportunity to observe and to write down whatever served my purpose, just as I had already done during my journeys everywhere in foreign parts. Between the home affairs I was allowed to see the Bishops of *Osnabrück* and *Paderborn* and to make etchings of their antiquities. In *Brussels* and *Antwerp* I made many works, I had to look over *Turnhout*, *Breda* and other frontier places, and – with the Commanders of the German Order of Knighthood – I could observe the nearest boundary between the United Provinces and *Germany*, just as the environs of *Zutphen*, *Overijssel* and *Drenthe* while attending to the Commissionership of *Lingen* for King *William* whose great memory will last for centuries.

The Court at *"The Loo"* also procured me to follow rather circumstantial information of a few affairs about some of our Provinces during which one could meet the noblest and most distinguished inhabitants at that place. These preparations showed me a paved way for the execution of my purpose and ever since when I found burghers and foreigners in difficulties, contracting an inheritance in or outside *Holland*, collecting debts, or attending to other interests, I have been pleased to add, at the service of natives and foreigners, the tribunals, the charters and laws, the times and manners of justice now in vogue in all Provinces. But if I were called to the bench and should have to join the Tribunal of any particular town and any village or manor, I should hardly find myself capable by half to execute what was required and the work of such a great outline that I should have to deal with it in two volumes; of which this one is the first, including the seven free United Provinces and the landscape, brought-to-light antiquities and histories of each one to show everybody, by the coherence of the times, why the United Netherlands certainly are in the righteous possession of their time-honoured freedom, so general in these countries as is elsewhere slavery, when anyone can see how those people, united in a sevenfold bond, have had honest protagonists to save their freedom, when suppressed, from the snares and fetters of the powerful from time immemorial. Thus his heart should be at rest with the governing members of that prospering State and it should ignite to support, with person and property, that government to equal, with the thriving of the community, the old inheritance which has to be brought up to date and polished preciously and they have to watch carefully that every land and town according to its character is well governed in both civil and legal affairs and these two make it possible to enjoy prosperity of body and soul, each according to his own standing, in a quiet and safe life.

Turn over the leaves of one or another of the described provinces and soon a most blessed change between the previous centuries and the present one will become clear; revolt, tyranny, murder, ravage and poverty has set in almost everywhere but for the few periods of quiet or prosperity. Fratricide, civil war, interior fighting, surprise attacks from abroad and despair of deliverance demolished castles, boroughs and cities, burned the land, destroyed generations, plundered the rivers and marauded the inner and outer waters. The foreign stadtholders fleeced their soldiers, flayed the desperate inhabitant and, did he look for rescue, he had to suffer as a recalcitrant; the religious coercion and the Bloody Council strengthened the frivolous life of grindingdown papists, the stake was the wages for reading the

ten, de tyden en manieren van Rechtsvorderingen over alle de Provincien nu in zwang, daar by te voegen : Maar wanneer ik even ingescheept was, en tot elken byzondere Stad, en yder Dorps of Heerlykheyds Vierschaar moet toe treden, vond ik myn naauwlyks half in staat om uyt te voeren, 't geen 'er vereyscht wierd, en van zo grooten omtrek het werk, dat ik het in Twee Deelen moet behandelen; van de welke dit het eerfte is, vervattende de zeven vrye Vereenigde Nederlanden, en yders Landschap, eerst opgedolve oudheden, en geschiedenissen, om door de zamenhang der tyden, elk een te doen zien, waarom de Verbonde Landen gewislyk staan in een rechtveerdig bezit van haar aaloude vryheyd, den Landen alhier zo algemeen, als elders de verslaaftheyd; wanneer een yder ziet, hoe brave Voorvechters die Volkeren, welke in een zevenbond verknocht zyn, van onheuglyke eeuwen, gehad hebben, om de zelve vryheyd, als ze gedrukt wierd te redderen, uyt de lagen, of boeyens der Geweldenaars, zo moet zyn hert op deze nu Regerende Leden van die Bloeyende Staat gerust zyn, en ontsteken, om met lyf en goed, die Regeering by te staan, welke de oude Herkomens, met het welvaren van 't gemeen, zo net evenaren, 't geen na vereysch der tyden, verschaaft moet werden, zo eel polysten, en zorgvuldig toezien dat yder Land en Stad, na zyn aard, ten beste werde bestiert in beyde Borgerlyke en Gerichtzaken en die beyde, om in een stil en veylig leven, elk na zyn stand, te doen genieten haar welvaart aan ziel en Lichaam.

Doorbladert, de eene en de andere der beschrevene Landen eens, aanstonds komt voor, een aldergelukzaligste verandering van de voorige eeuwen tot de tegenwoordige; Oproer, Dwingelandy, Moord, Verwoesting, en Armoede, is by na over al ingevallen, op de weynige tyden van rust of welvaren. Broedermoord, Burgerkryg, Binnenlandsche oorlog, Buytenlandsche overval en wanhoop van uytkomst, sloopten de Sloten, Vlekken en Steden, verbranden het platte Land, verdelgden de Geslachten, beplunderden de Stroomen, en stroopten de binnen en buyten golven. De Vremde Stadhouders plukten, haar Soldaten vilden, den hopelozen inwoonder, en zach hy om na reddering, zo leed hy als een weerspanneling; de Geloofsdwang en Bloedraad steevigde het wuft leven der uytmergelende Papen, de Brandpaal,

* *

was

was 't loon van de Heylige Bladen te lezen, en de ſtrop ſtond op een geeſtlyk lied. Katten en Honden had de benaaude Borger niet genoeg om ſtandvaſtig die Rampen tegen te ſtaan, of ploy-de hy door de honger, zo moeſt hy de kop aan 't zwaard geven, of rug aan rug gebonden in 't water ſmooren.

Maar de Almogende zy dank, door die Helden welke de qua-den zo hebben gebraveerd; en die welke nu zo ernſtig en Man-lyk den Staat, met wyze Hoofden en koene herten opvoeren, boven het zo lang, rondom ons knagende geweld. Die ware Vaders, van het vrye ja Zegenvyerende Vaderland, geven ons een gewiſſe hoop van een gulde eeuw, waar in de Vrede en Ge-rechtigheyd malkander zullen ontmoeten, om de ware Gods-dienſt te ſtaven, verzekerd met de Vryheyd der Landen in de Aaloude Eendragt, en de zelve doen uytbazuynen, de zegenen die zy ontfangt na de beloften over de verborgentheyd der on-gerechtigheden; zy doen ons zien de krachtigſte onderſcheyden der toeſtand, van die quade tot deze beter tyden. De Zeven Ver-eenigde Landen zeegepralende, met zo veel voordeel op hare Vy anden; de Landſchappen yder in een bloeyende overvloed van alles, de verafgelegenſte Zeên van hare Schepen bevaren, de nieuwe Werreld voor een groot deel haar onderdanig met het geluk van daar het zaligmakende woord te verkondigen, en de zielen der vreemde Volkeren in te oogſten. De Steden verre meeſt boven de helft vergroot, en wel eens zo veel verheerlykt: van waar komen deze zegeningen, wy genietenze onver-diend! maar derft men zich wat vleyen, zo zynze ſtaatkundiglyk onſcheydbaar vaſt, aan de heerlyke vryheyd en gerechtigheyd, die hier hare Tempelen geſticht hebben; en deze twee Godin-nen kanmen niet kennen, als uyt de aanmerkingen die men maakt op de Regeering van deze Landen, welke aanſtonds ons brengt tot de beſpiegeling van de heerlyke, vrye, en zuyvere manier, der verkiezingen onzer Vroedſchappen en Raden, de mond des Volks, dat als eertyds *Iſrael*, God alleen tot heerſcher kent; en van die Raden wederom de beſtellingen der Burgermeeſteren en Schepenen, om de zaken van yder Stad en hare Rechtbanken waar te nemen, met drie Gemeentsluyden of andere bedienden welke de laſten en verzochte inlagen der Borgers tot des Staats behoef bezorgen, en waken voor de Weduwen, Weezen, en Armen,

Holy Script and a sacred song was liable to be punished by the hangman's rope. The fearful burgher did not have sufficient cats and dogs to survive and to withstand those calamities firmly, or should he yield from hunger, he had to give his head to the sword or suffocate, tied back to back, in the water.

But thanks to the Almighty for the heroes who resisted the evils; and who now raise the state so gravely and manly with wise heads and brave hearts above the violence which preyed around us so long. Those true fathers of the free and triumphant home-land give us a certain hope of a golden age in which peace and justice will meet to substantiate the true religion, ensured by the freedom of the countries in time-honoured union, and to blazon forth the blessings they receive after the promises of the hidden iniquities; they make us see the strongest differences in the situation from those evil to these better times. The Seven United Provinces triumphant with so many advantages over her enemies; the regions each in a flowering abundance of ever-ything, the far-away seas sailed by her ships, the New World, for a great part, submissive, with the good fortune of preaching there the soul-saving Word, and harvesting the souls of foreign peoples. The towns mostly half enlarged and twice as magni-ficent again; from where do these blessings come, we enjoy them undeservedly! But if one dares to flatter oneself, they are politically inseparably fixed to the glorious freedom and justice which have founded their temples here; and one cannot know these two goddesses but for the considerations of the govern-ment of these Provinces which brings us forthwith to the contemplation of the glorious, free and pure manner of the election of our Corporations and Councils, the mouthpieces of the people who, as in former times in *Israel,* know only God as their ruler; and again from those councils the appointments of the burgomasters and magistrates to attend to the affairs of each town and its tribunals together with three town-councillors and other clerks who take care of the charges and requested deposits of the burghers towards the needs of the state and watch over the widows, orphans and the impoverished; who, in the meeting

PREFACE

of the States deliberate, debate and execute the affairs of land and sea, the necessity of armies and fleets and to equip the military stores, to promote peace and pacts, to keep coinage pure and to maintain dykes, roads, beaches, frontier-places and the towns conquered with joint weapons; to settle everybody's rights in disputes, to help the burdened once or more than once in Higher Courts and not to tolerate that anyone more powerful should suppress and torture – as in former times – his inferior, or with internal force rob the impoverished of his possession. These glorious, even divine things are the subject of this first volume and the second one will deal with the affairs depending on their High Mightiness the States General, which I have not wanted to touch upon in this first part. They will not have to be less important than this part. I have done this work for my own pleasure on festival days and without being otherwise engaged by more important matters. Who feels so inclined can read this in the same way or leave it if he has more useful or necessary things to do. In the extremity of distress to consult how to behave in his lawsuits here or elsewhere and then finding to his satisfaction how to advance his affairs, he will find my hours well spent according to the duty of

a willing fellow-citizen, compatriot and honest friend,

ROMEYN DE HOOGHE

VOOR-REEDEN.

Armen; die in der Staten vergadering beraadſlagen, overleggen en uytvoeren tot Land en Zeezaken, het noodige van Legers, Vlooten, en Krygsvoorraad toe doen ruſten, Vrede en Verbonden maken, zuyvere munt houden, Dyken, Wegen, Stranden, Grensplaatzen en die met de gemeene Wapens, gewonne Steden in ſtaat en ſtand houden; of yders regt in geſchillen afdoen, de bezwaarde eens en meermalen met hoger Banken te goede komen, en niet dulden, dat yder magtigerzyn minder, als eertyds drukke en folteren, of met Binnenlands geweld den armen 't zyne ontrove. Deze heerlyke ja Godlyke zaken zyn 't onderwerp van dit eerſte Deel, en het tweede zal alzo behandelen de zaken welke van de algemeyne Staten hare Hoogmogende af hangen, aan de welke ik in dit eerſte Lit, niet heb willen raaken, zullende van geen geringer ommeſlag als dit deel moeten zyn; ik heb deze zaken voor myn eygen luk, op vierdagen en zonder belet van noodzakelyker gedaan, die 't luſt kan ook zo dezelve lezen, en laten 't na als hy nutter of nodiger te doen heeft. Tot hem de nood prangt, om na te zien hoe hy zich in zyne Rechtsgedingen hier of elders moet dragen, zyn genoegen tot vordering zyner zaken, dan vindende, zo zal hy myne uyren beſteed vinden na de plicht van

een bereydwillig Medeborger, genegen Landsgenoot en eerlyk Vriend,

ROMEYN DE HOOGHE

** 2   Tot

SPIEGEL van STAAT

DER

VEREENIGDE

NEDERLANDEN.

EERSTE HOOFDSTUK.

Gelegentheyd der Vereenigde Nederlanden, met haar aard en imborst.

ET Deel van Europaas vaste Land, welk tegen over Brittanniën legt, van ouds Batavia of Phræsia genaamd, is nu het Vereenigde Nederland; zynde nu dezelve Volkeren, in een Bondgenootschap, dewelke eerst met de Roomse Monarchy, als in Broeder en Bondgenootschap, op beroemde Naam deeden onderscheyden. Maar naderhand, om des selfs dwingelandy, met overwinnende Wapenen, tegen die Machten wereld-ruchtig gemaakt, volgens de getuygenis van de Vyandlyke Schryvers. Uyt de Duytzen herkomstig zyn ze door Burgertwist, van de Catten of Hessen geschift, en hebben de laatste deelen van Gallien, leeg van Inwoonders, beslagen. Met het Eyland welk door het splyten der Rhyn, van die

De Stand der Zeeven Vereenigde Landen in Europa.

I. Deel.   A   schey-

MIRROR OF STATE

OF THE

UNITED

NETHERLANDS

FIRST CHAPTER.

Situation of the United Netherlands and its character and disposition.

The part of Europe's mainland situated opposite Britain, of old called Batavia or Phraesia, is now the United Netherlands, consisting of the same peoples who, in an alliance at first with the Roman Catholic Monarchy in community and confederacy, distinguished themselves by their famous name. But later on, because of the tyranny of that monarchy, with victorious arms against those powers, that name was made notorious according to the evidence of hostile authors. Of German origin they have been divided by civil dissension of the "Cats" or Hessians and they have occupied the last parts of Gaul, empty of inhabitants, together with the island which, by bifurcation of the Rhine, goes from that division as far as the sea, and besides Over-Yssel, Zutphen, Friesland, Drenthe, Twenthe, Groningen and Ommelanden.

The outermost fringe of these lands belongs to the combined Seven United Provinces, now called the lands and districts of the States General. These may be compared with Outer Possessions and the Seven Provinces with the towns.

The seven lands are: GELDERLAND, HOLLAND, ZEELAND, FRIESLAND, UTRECHT, OVERYSSEL, GRONINGEN.

The lands of the States General are, on the coast on the Flemish side and South of the Scheldt, Sluis and Hulst, besides many entrenchments of name and size such as Isabelle, Sas van Gent, entrenchments near Hulst and near Axel, at Cadzand, Philippynen, Liefkenshoek; inland of the Scheldt Lillo, Zandvliet, the Marquisate of Bergen-op-Zoom and Wouw, the Barony of Breda, the Bailiwick of Bois-le-Duc, Maastricht and the landed properties of Valkenburg, Peel, the Campine, de Graaf, Overmaas, Roermond, Venlo, Stevenswaard, Coevorden, the Bourtange, Lier and Lieroort, Deylerschans, Huys ten Noord and the garrison at Embden.

The periphery of all these lands was surrounded, at the north west, by the Ocean or the North Sea, which, coming from behind Scotland and checked by the bulging coastline at Calais and Dover against the waters of the Spanish Sea flowing through the Channel and strengthened there by the Irish Sea or St. George's Channel, washing ashore much sand along our coasts leaving it there and making a rough seabed full of reefs and banks, was only navigable through fairways and estuaries which change very often and demand constant observation and new buoys and beacons; wherein lies a certain strength and power of these lands since no enemy can attempt any landing on these shores without the utmost danger, nor can he stay so near the beach that he could protect the disembarkation of his soldiers by the guns of his ships. Thus the invasion of the rivermouths, or estuaries with a fleet is also subjected too much to inevitable harm, apart from the fact that one cannot possibly find more unsettled wind and weather anywhere else than on these shores

---

fcheyding tot de Zee loopt, en voorts Over-Yffel, Zutfen, Vriefland, Drent, Twent, Groningen en Ommelanden.

De buytenfte Zoom dezer Landen, behoort aan de gefamentlyke Zeeven Verbonde Landen; nu Generaliteyts Landen en Diftricten genaamd. Deze zyn als de Buytenwerken, en de zeeven Provintien als de Stad,

Namen der zeven Landen. De zeeven Landen zyn, GELDERLAND, HOLLAND, ZEELAND, VRIESLAND, UYTRECHT, OVERYSSEL, GRONINGEN.

Stand en benaming der Generaliteyts. Landen. De Landen der Generaliteyt zyn aan de Zee, na de Vlaamfe zyde Sluys, Hulft, over de Schelde, neveus veele Schanfen van Naam en groote, als Ifabelle, Sas van Gent, Schanfen by Hulft en by Axel, in Cadfand, Philippynen, Liefkenshoek; binnen 't Scheld, Lillo, Santvliet, Marquifaat van Bergen op Zoom en Wouw, de Baronnye van Breda, de Meyery van 's Hertogenbofch, Maeftricht en Landen van Valkenburg, Peel, Kempen, de Graaf, Overmaas, Ruremond, Venlo, Stevenswaerd; Coeverden, de Bourtang, Lier en Lieroort, Deylerfchans, Huys te Noord, de bezetting in Embden.

Den ommekreits van alle deze Landen, werd omringeld, in 't Noordweften met den Oceaan of Noordzee, welke achter Schotland om komende, en ftuytende aan de Hoofden, tuffen Cales en Douvres, tegen den invloet der Wateren van de Spaanfe Zee, door 't Canaal gevloeyt, en daar in verfterkt door de Yerfe Zee, of 't Canaal van St. Joris, hier langs onze Kuften veel Sand aanfpoelende, laat fitten, en maakt een vuyle Grond, vol riffen en banken, alleen by floven en gaten in te Lootfen, die zeer dikmaals veranderende, geduurig opmerken, en nieuwe tonnen en bakens eyfcht; waar in een gewiffe kracht en fterkte dezer Landen is geleegen, dewyl geen Vyand zonder het uyterfte gevaar aan deze Stranden, eenige Landingen onderneemen kan, noch het ftrand zo na by blyven, dat hy het Landen van fijn Krygsvolk kan vryen door 't Gefchut van zyne Scheepen. Alzoo is ook het invallen met een Vloot in de Monden of Zeegaten, te veel onvermydelyke quaden onderworpen, behalven dat men mogelyk nergens vind een ongeftadiger weer en wind, als op deze Kuften, en

een

een wind uyt den Noordweſten, zou een gantſche Vloot ſloopen, gelyk deze Landen aan haar eygen Vloot van Gottenburg komende, met ſwaare Schipbreuken, en oneyndige Drenkelingen gezien hebben. Dan hebben zy tot Buuren aan de Franſe zyde de Vlamingen, het Marquiſaat van Antwerpen, Brabant, Luyk, Keulen, Kleef, Gulik, Lingen, Munſterland, Weſtphalen, en Ooſt-Vrieſland : de Maas en Rhyn dekken eenigzins dezelve met de Eems, en voorts de moeraſſige Heyden van de Bourtang, tot dicht aan de Zutphenſe randen, en wederom een diergelyke Heyde, tuſſchen Nimwegen en Mook, en diergelyke van de Peel en Kempen : maar de onſterffelyke Bouwmeeſter Koehoorn, heeft verſchyde Lynen aan den Staat vertoont, om de Hoofd ommekrits te konnen dras leggen, en de reſt met wel verſterkte Steeden bewaren. Van ouds waren deze Landen aldus bekent.

Bataven Cananifates Friſiabones, zyn nu Zuyd-Holland en Weſt-Vrieſland; daar by komende Medenblik Enkhuyzen, Hoorn, en haare onderhoorigheden : van de Graven van Holland ondergebragt, en haar aan Holland gehegt.

Sicambroſen, Bataven. *Geldubiſe*, zyn Gelderland. *Uſipiën* de Zutphenſe.

Mattiaci, Zeeland.

Friſen zyn noch by dezelve naam beroemd, maar ingekrompen.

Marſen en *Trajectynen*, het Sticht en de Veluw.

Phileum of *Phylleum*, Groningen.

Cauci Emden, *Amſibari*, 't Volk om Lier Bourtang, enz.

Tencteri de Drent. *Tubantes* de Twent. *Chamavi*, de Wolden, en rondom deze de *Bructeri*, de Moeraſſige Heyden, van de Bourtang, Coeverden en Noorthorn bewoonende.

Gugernen, Kleefſe en Gulikſe.

Eburonen, Peelſe en Kempenaars, ten tyden van Keyzer *Julianus*, ingeſchikt van de Bataven, om daar in te ontfangen de *Salien*, die rondom den Yſel en Rhyn, zo aan de eene als de andere zyde haar neder ſloegen, en de *Quaden*, die de Peel landen en de Kempen, met de Meyery beſloegen, en een gemeyne beſt met ons maakten, dezelve naam van *Bataven* dragende. A 2 *Tun-*

[margin note:] Beſchryving der Namen dezer Landen van Ouds, en derzelver tegenwoordige benaming.

and a wind from the north-west would break up a whole fleet as these lands with their own fleet coming from Gothenburg have experienced with heavy shipwreck and an enormous number drowned. Furthermore they have, on the French side, the Flemish as neighbours and the Marquisate of Antwerp, Brabant, Liège, Cologne, Cleves, Juliers, Lingen, Munsterland, Westphalia and East Friesland; the Meuse and the Rhine more or less protect these regions together with the Eems, and moreover the marshy moorland of the Bourtange as far as the border of Zutphen and once again a similar morass between Nimeguen and Mook and again a similar area of the Peel and the Campine; but the renowned architect Coehoorn has demonstrated various ways of inundating the main boundaries and to save the rest with well fortified towns. Thus these provinces were known from time immemorial.

Bataven Cananifates Frisiabones, are now called South-Holland and West-Friesland; moreover Medemblik, Enkhuizen, Hoorn and their dependencies subjected and attached to Holland by the Counts of Holland.

Sicambrosen, Batavians. *Geldubise*, Gelderland. *Usipiën*, Zutphen. *Mattiaci*, Zeeland. The Frisians are still famous by the same name but they have dwindled down. *Marsen* and *Trajectynen*, the Veluwe and the bishopric of Utrecht. *Phileum* or *Phylleum*, Groningen. *Cauci*, Emden. *Amsibari*, the people round Lier Bourtange, & c.

Tencteri, Drenthe. *Tubantes*, Twenthe. *Chamavi*, the Wolds and around these the *Bructeri*, who live in the marshy moorland of the Bourtange, Coevorden and Noordhorn. *Gugernes*, Cleves and Juliers.

Eburones, the people of the Peel and the Campine, who, in the days of the Emperor *Julianus*, yielded to the Batavians to receive the *Salians*, who around the Yssel and the Rhine defeated them on one side as well as on the other, and the *Quaden* who occupied the Peel region and the Campine together with the Bailiwick formed a commonwealth with us bearing the same name of *Batavians*.

MIRROR of STATE

Tungren, are the people of Tongeren, almost the same name. *Condrusi*, those of Condros, *Betasieu*, en *Menapiën* under the same name. *Adriatise*, the inhabitants of Antwerp, Turnhout and the regions around it. *Nerveën*, the people around the Scheldt. *Taxandren*, Cadzand, Sluis and environs. *Morinen*, the inhabitants of the coast between Calais and Sluis.

To enlighten the mind while reading I felt inclined to show, in these few lines, the old names against those known at present.

Of most of these peoples it is surprising that they have defended – stubbornly and gloriously – the freedom in which they lived in Germany, according to the law of nature, while the neighbouring peoples were overpowered by Romans, Swabians, Cimbres, Goths and Norsemen. Yes, even the large islands of Britain or England and Scotland, along with Ireland, Iceland &c, were labouring under the Roman yoke or forced to leave their abodes after having been plundered by Picts, Danes and Norsemen.

Although they differ considerably in character among themselves they nevertheless agree when it comes to maintaining their state and position up to the last drop of blood and the last penny of their purse.

They differ slightly in their way of government but together they have an intense driving-force against a one-headed supremacy and they each keep strictly to their old way of arrangements in the governments of the towns and rural districts; and also their kind of charges as those they have to pay to the States General as well as those which serve to the maintenance of the necessary works in each "province". This foreign name is given to these lands peculiarly enough, meaning with the Latins a conquered region, subordinated to them and ruled in their manner by proconsuls, legates or other superintendants who wielded power over those lands according to the will of the Roman council and people. This could never have been said of these lands, but the word "province" is so generally accepted for these areas

---

Tungren, zyn de Tongerfe met dezelve naam *Condrufi*, die van Condros *Betafieu* en *Menapiën*, onder dezelve.

Adriatife, de Antwerpenaars, Turnhoutfe en daar rondom.

Nerveën, de Inwoonders om de Schelde.

Taxandren, Cadfant, Sluys en Bylanden.

Morinen, de Zeeftrand-bewoonders van Cales tot Sluys.

Om in het leezen de gedachten op te helderen, heeft my geluft deze wynige regulen weegens de oude benamingen tegen de tegenwoordige bekende namen te doen zien

Aard van 't Volk. Van de meefte dezer Volkeren, is verwonderens waardig, dat zy de Vryheid, met dewelke zy in Duytfchland na de richtfnoer der Natuur leefden, hardnekkig en roemryk hebben verdeedigd, terwyl, de nabuurige Volkeren door de Romeynen, Swaben, Cimbren, Gotten, en Noormannen, over-ftroomd wierden. **Tegen geweld buytenlands.** Ja zelfs de groote Eylanden van Brittanniën of Engeland en Schotland, nevens Ierland, Yfland, enz. onder 't Roomfe jok bukten, of van Picten, Deenen en Nooren geplunderd, haare Wooningen moeften verlaten.

Binnenlands. Zy zy wel veel onder een van aard verfchillende, maar nogtans daar in te zamen eens, om haar ftand en ftaat tot de laatfte droppel bloeds, en de laatfte penning van haar beurs te handhaven.

Verfchil en inschikking. Zy verfchillen eenigzins van malkanders vorm van beftier, maar hebben te zamen een ingefpanne drift, tegen een eenhoofdige Oppermacht, en houden yders ftreng vaft in haar oude wyze van befchik in de Regeeringen, der Steeden en ten platte Landen. Als mede haar foort van Laften, zo die, welke zy voor den algemeenen Staat moeten opbrengen, als die welke dienen tot onderhoud van de nodige Werken, in yders Provintie. Deze onduytfe naam is zeer oneygen aan deze Landen gegeeven, beteekenende by de Latynen een aangewonnen Landftreek, onder hun gebracht, en geregeld na haare wyfen onder Proconfuls, Legaten, of andere Opper-Intendanten, welke de Oppermacht in die Landen oeffende, na de wil des Roomfchen Raads en Volks, 't geen van deze Landen noyt heeft konnen gezegt werden; maar 't woord van Provincie is zo gemeen ontfangen voor deze Landen , dat men daar van zich moet bedienen, om bywylen de duyfterheyt te ontgaan. Men vind het ten minften al te veel by Spaanfe , Italiaanfe, Franfe , Engelfe en andere Schryvers, om het gants ongeraakt voorby te gaan.

De Manfchap van alle deze Landen is ftrydbaar, maar de eene der Provintien fteekt meer uit te Land , en de andere wederom ter Zee, welke te zamen een geduchte Macht uytleveren; en tot malkanders hulp bereydwillig toe treeden. Meeft fterk , wel gemaakt en leerzaam. *De Manfchap.*

De Vrouwen zyn neerftig, net in haar Huyshouding, mal goed met de Kinderen, voor welke men haar ziet alle krachten infpannen, en de meefte zelf in 't midden der middelen fchraal leeven , om hun kracht te verryken en te veel gemak naar te laten. *Neerftigheyd. Netheyd.*

Beyde de kunne is bequaam tot Koopmanfchappen , Winkel-neering en Handwerken; vroeg en laat aan 't werk , fcherp in de opmerking van haar beurs ; eertyds veel meer oprecht, nu door de konftenaryen der Vreemdelingen , al wat van de uyterfte deugd afgeweeken , en wat minder eenvoudig. *Luft tot handel.*

Noch fteeken Mannen en Vrouwen uyt in Kuysheyt tegen andere haare Nabuuren; hoewel de goede zeeden , (God betert) te mets wat dunder te vinden zyn, door 't gemak en de weelde verbafterende , en vaak beftormt door de wufte wildwaeyigheyd der Buytenlanders, *Kuysheid.*

Het weeten, en leezen tot Geleerdheyt toe, der Talen die niet als aan de Hooge Schoolen geoeffend werden, is hier zo gemeen, dat veele Vrouwen ook Latyn, of Grieks , of Hebreeuws willen fchynen te kennen; door de Godsdienft aangezet, of Geeftelyke hovaardigheyd. Ja, men vind 'er Vrouwen, die om na te fpooren , de Goddelyke huyshoudinge, haar eygene wat loffer behandelen. *Weetgierigheyt.*

Zy zyn vry minder bygelovig als veele Volkeren, zo dat men in de Zeeven Landen, noch toveren, noch mirakelen ziet, en de verfchyningen van Geeften, Spoken en Kaboutermannekens, zyn daar praatjens voor de fpinrok van flechte Wyfjens. Ja 't loopt gevaar , of 't gemeen niet al te zeer word ont- *Niet bygelovig.*

A 3

that one has to use it to escape vagueness at times. At least one finds it only too often used by Spanish, Italian, French, English and other authors to pass over it entirely.

The men of all these regions are combative but in some of the provinces they are more excellent ashore and in others afloat, so together they supply a formidable force, ready to render each other assistance. They are mostly strong, well-built and docile.

The women are dilligent, tidy in their housekeeping, far too good to the children, for whom they exert all their strength and most of them live frugally even in the midst of plenty to enrich their power and to obviate too much comfort.

Both sexes are competent in trade, shopkeeping and crafts; early and late at work, keeping a sharp eye on their purse; formerly far more honest, now, through the tricks of foreigners, already deviating somewhat from the utmost virtue and slightly less simple.

Men and women still compare favourably with the neighbouring peoples as to modesty, although the good morals (God forbid!) gradually become somewhat scarcer and deteriorated through love of ease and prosperity and often badly influenced by the frivolity of foreigners.

Knowledge and reading, up to the learning of languages only taught at the universities, is so general here that many women also seem to want to be acquainted with Latin, Greek or Hebrew either stimulated by religion or by intellectual pride. Yes, one comes across women who treat their own household more loosely to be able to investigate the Divine order.

They are a good deal less superstitious than other peoples so that, in the Seven Provinces, one sees neither witchcraft nor miracles and the apparitions of ghosts, spooks and goblins are only gossip of simple women at the distaff. Yes, there is a danger that the community is too much relieved of the disturbing fear of

MIRROR of STATE

devils, ogres and fiends.

Nowhere is there, amongst merchants, such a great readiness to trust their goods to foreigners and compatriots, although the continual wars, the piracy and robbery of the enemies have ruined many of them. The splendour and frivolity, not decreased through the falling off of profits and many losses suffered from these wrongs, have restrained such unlimited confidence; nevertheless there always are venturesome people, so tempted by profits, that a foreigner who has paid twice, establishes confidence for longterm debts, which, as one sees to one's surprise, run out to twenty or more months in some places, to get a bit more rather than a ready payment. Meanwhile the economy in the home makes this reproach bearable and with this trustful persuasion they certainly find acceptance in many places where the English, French, Germans or Italians cannot or do not want to trade.

In the country and in the towns one very often meets with double profits. The women in the towns keep shops or carry on trade for one or another factory while the men pursue their profits abroad; the country people and those along the coasts of Holland, Zeeland and Friesland sail to every region while agriculture is not neglected by women and children.

The haughty Greeks and Romans called other peoples Barbarians as the Jews called them Goim, labouring under the delusion that only they themselves had wisdom and intelligence, everybody else being excluded, so that they did not scruple to describe the Batavian as rude, obtuse and unteachable along with the Swiss although they nevertheless liked to use them in the art of war and, during the insurrection of Claudius Civilis for freedom, they complained about the slyness of his intellect and all the tricks he used for feigning and disguising. It should be added that they gave the best part of Britain to a descendant of the same Civilis to rule. But one of the most alert Frenchmen

---

ontheven van de laftige vrees voor Duyvels, Bytebauwen en Nickers.

Vertrou-wen.

Nergens vindmen by de Kooplieden zo grooten gereedheyd om aan buyten en binnenlanders haare Goederen te vertrouwen, hoewel de geduurige Oorlogen, de Kaperyen en Roveryen der Vyanden, veele heeft gekraakt, en de pracht en wuftheyd niet vermindert, met het ontfchieten der winften, en uyt deze quaden, veele fchaden geleeden zynde, zoodanig wyduytloopend vertrouwen hebben beteugeld; nochtans zyn 'er steeds waaghalzen, welke de winft zo verlokt, dat een Vreemdeling tweemaal wel betaalende, vertrouwen veft, voor lange fchuldloop, die men op fommige plaatzen tot verwondering ziet, op twintig en meer Maanden uytloopen, om een kleyntjen meer, liever als de veerdige af betaling. De zuynigheyt van de keuken maakt ondertuffen dit verwyt verdraaglyk, en zeeker met dit vertrouwend inpalmen vinden zy ingang in veele plaatzen, waar op Engelfe, Franfe, Duytfen of Italianen, niet konnen of willen handelen.

Arheyd-zaamheyt.

Men vind by de Landzaten en in de Steeden zeer gemeen dobble winften, de Vrouwen in de Steeden doen Winkels of Hanteeringen, die aan de eene of de andere Fabryken dienen, terwyl de Mannen buyten 's Lands haare winften opfpeuren; de Land- en Strand lieden van Holland, Zeeland en Vriesland, varen na alle Geweften ter Zee, terwyl de Landbouw van de Vrouwen en Kinderen niet en werd verfuymt.

Schrander-heyd.

De hovaerdige Grieken en Romeynen noemden de andere Volkeren Barbaren, gelyk de Joden Goim, waanende dat zy alleen bezaaten wysheyt en verftand, met uytfluyting van de reft, zo datze haar niet ontzagen den Batavier voor rouw, bot en onleerfaam te befchryven, nevens de Switfer, daar ze nochtans in konft van Oorlogen geerne zich van die bedienden; en in den opftand van Claudius Civilis voor de Vryheyt, klaagden over de gefleepenheyd van zyn verftand, en de meefte ftreeken waar van hy zich in 't veynfen en ontveynfen bediende, waar by men noch moet zetten, dat ze een Naneef van deze Civilis, het befte deel van Brittanniën te regeeren gaven; maar een der wakkerfte Franfen in 't befchryven van een Mi-

nifter

nifter van Staat, laat zich daar op in zyn Voor-reeden uyt, wegens de Hollanders aldus. Maar de laatfte (fpreekende van de Helvetiers en Bataven) hebben die naam lang afgelegd, en verdienen nu dat wy na haare Hooge Schoolen gaan, haar fcherpfinnigheyt en goed oordeel met verwondering hooren, en in onze Schriften haare groote Mannen als fteunfels van onze gedachten invoeren.

't Is ook niet te ontkennen dat Taalkunde, Vrye Konften, *Oeffeningen in Talen en Wetenfchappen.* zeldzaame Gereedfchappen, en alle Mechanife toeftel, hier wonderlyk bloeijen. Dat deze Landen uyt de natuur, byzonder in Waterland, Wiskonftenaars by uytnementheyt aanqueken; dat in hare Steeden alle de Laken- en Stofwerken, alle Twyn- en Garenwerken, by uytneementheyt werden in top gevoerd, 't zy van fynigheyt, 't zy van lichtheyt, met zo behagelyke kennis in 't fchakeeren der Verwen, zoo fchoone fwier van omtrek, en alles of met zo nette hand, voor dierbaare Stoffen, of met zo luchtigen aard voor de goedkoop, datze de Vreemdelingen dwingen, haare Stoffen en Goederen voor anderen te neemen.

Waar by komende de ongelooffelyke Volkrykheyd, en de behoeftigheyt van toevoer uyt andere Landen, deze altyd in ftaat zyn, Koopmanfchap tegen Koopmanfchap, en Waren tegen Waren te wiffelen, of trocqueeren.

Deze Volkeren zyn niet zeer fchielyk in toorn, ten zy by *Lydzaamheyd.* fterk Bier, Wyn of Brandewyn, in welke zich veele van de jonge jaaren af, al wat fterk te buyten gaan; doch buyten dit quaad, zynze laauw tegen ongelyk dat ze ontfangen; zo wel yder in zyn byzonder, als wel voornamentlyk de Volkeren zamen in haar zevenvoudig Verbond, eensdeels om de natuurlyke ingebooren imborft, anderdeels om dat de zamengevloeide Lichamen uyt verfcheyde Landen, in welker gezamentlyke Vergadering, door overreeding alleen, en niet door ontzag kan werden gewerkt: en welker Leeden rugfpraak met haare Heeren en Meefters, de Souverainen van elke Provintie, moeten houden, die zeer verfchyde belangen hebbende, ook noodzakelyk langzamer beradingen en gevolgelyk uytvoeringen hebben moeten. Maar dezelve koele gemoederen, zo men: het

describing a Minister of State, gives his opinion about this in his preface thus, in an account of the Hollanders. But the latter (talking about the Helvetians and the Batavians) have laid aside that name long ago and they now deserve that we go to their universities, listen to their intelligence and good reason in wonder and that we introduce their great men as help for our thoughts.

It also cannot be denied that philology, the liberal arts, rare instruments and all mechanical apparatus flourish wonderfully here. These provinces breed, from nature, especially in watery country, excellent mathematicians. In their towns all cloth factories and all twining- and spinning-mills were developed to extreme excellence, be it in fineness, be it in lightness, with such pleasant knowledge of the gradation of colours and such beautiful design and everything sewn very neatly for expensive materials, or so lightly for the cheaper ones that foreigners simply have to buy their materials and goods here in preference to elsewhere.

There has to be added the unbelievably large population and the necessity to import from other countries always capable of exchange or barter business for business and goods for goods.

These peoples are not easily infuriated unless drinking strong beer, wine or brandy of which many people drink too much from their youngest days. But apart from this vice they are lukewarm towards the wrongs done to them, each one in particular as well as, especially, the peoples altogether in their sevenfold alliance, partly because of their inborn disposition, partly because in the joint Assembly, composed of the united bodies from the various provinces, it is only possible to work with persuasion and not by authority; and their members have to consult with their lords and masters, the rulers of each province, who, having very different interests, necessarily must have slower deliberations and consequently slower execution. But the same cool minds, when one considers the people, are

MIRROR of STATE

heated to the utmost brutality when their patience is tried too long and it explodes into rage. They themselves are in the habit of comparing the temper of their inborn character with iron pots which take a long time to get completely hot and bring the liquid they hold to the boil, but once they are completely hot they boil with such fierceness and heat that it would be impossible to cool them down.

Generally one can find a persistency useful in the enterprises of trade and expeditions, in investigating and exploring the arts and inventions, in repairing locks, dykes, roads, fields, homesteads, in restarting shipping trade, in supporting wars, in enduring misery, as well as in sustaining and encouraging their fellow-citizens mainly in the first principles of freedom against the yoke of Spain, because of which they suffered arson, hunger, thirst, the plague, inundation of land, nullification of their debentures, dispersion of their families, yes, up to the last despair when business went completely down in the days of the Prince of Parma, namely when they had to pierce the dykes to inundate the whole country and had to save themselves in ships seeking safety in flight to foreign regions by trusting body, family and stock to the waves of the sea.

It has been remarked by Polybius that after the crushing defeat at Cannae, the Romans had nothing left but their obstinacy towards adversity; he would have said the same of these peoples, had he lived to see them united. For worn out by murderous massacres of the "Hoeksen and Cabeljause", "Heekerens and Batenburgers", "Schieringers and Vetkopers", (which the lords of the land possibly did not reckon to be too much against their interests) they were put to great expense by the wild expeditions of the Emperor Charles V; and after that from the Spanish war of eighty years, without time to breathe, into a Portuguese, an English, a Swedish and a Munster war. That Spanish war had affected the vital parts of the body of each province but the greatest danger was averted.

30

8 SPIEGEL van STAAT,

het Volk aanmerkt, zyn tot de uyterſte onmenſchelykheyt verhit, als haar gedult, te lang geperſt, tot raſerny uitbarſt. Zy zelve, zyn gewoon de tempering van haar ingebooren aart, te vergelyken by de yſere Potten, welke wel lang zyn, om door-heet te werden, en de vocht die ze bevatten, te doen kooken, maar zoo ze eens door-heet geworden zyn, zo kooken ze met zulken vinnigheyt en hitte, dat 'er geen koelen aan is.

Hardnec-kigheyd. In 't algemeen vind men een hardnekkigheyd, welke haar in de onderneemingen, van handel en tochten, in 't na en doorwroeten van Konſten en Uitvindingen, in 't hermaken van Sluyſen, Dyken, Wegen, Landen, Hofſteeden, in het hervatten van Rederyen, in 't uythouden van de Oorlogen, in 't doorſtaan der elenden; gelyk in 't opſcherpen en het aanmoedigen, van den eenen Medeborger tot den ander, voornamelyk in de eerſte beginzelen der Vryheid tegen het Jok van Spanjen. In deze leeden zy Brandſtichten, Honger, Dorſt, Peſt, onderlopen van Landen, vernietigen van hare Schuldbrieven, verſtroyen van haare Huysgezinnen, ja tot de laaſte wanhoop toe, wanneer de zaken, in de tyd van den Prinzen van Parma, zeer verliepen. Namentlyk, de Dyken door te ſteeken, het gantſche Land onder te doen lopen; zig in Scheepen te bergen, en om een goed heen komen te zoeken in vreemde geweſten lyf, gezin en haven aan de Zee-baren te vertrouwen.

'T is by Polybius aangemerkt, dat na de ſware neerlaag by Cannas, het Roomſche gebied niets behouden kon, als de hardnekkigheyd tegen de ongevallen : diergelyk had hy van deze volkeren gezegt, had hyze vereenigd beleefd. Want afgemat, door 't moorddadig bloetlaten der hoekze en Cabeljauſe, Heekerens en Batenburgers, Schieringers en Vetkopers, ('t geen de Lands-Heeren mogelyk niet al te zeer tegen hare belangen reekenden) vielen zy in de grote koſten der wilde tochten van Keyzer Karel de Vyfde; en daar uit in de Spaanzen Oorlog van tachtich Jaren, zonder azem te halen in een Portugeeze, Engelze, Sweedze en Munſterze Oorlog. Die Spaanzen Oorlog had de Edelſte deelen van 't Lighaam van yders Staat, aangetaſt; het grootſte gevaar wierd afge-ſtaan;

ſtaan; ja men zette een zeegen in het oorlogsvyer, men ſtrekte de landpalen wyd en zyd uit, zelf tot zulk een vergrooting dat men gedrongen wierd, ('t geen zelden beurt) om het al te zeer krimpen van onze vyands magt, vreede te maken. Maar daar quam op, die alderverſchriklykſte ſtorm, van Vrankryks woedende Heerſchſucht, die met drie leegers te gelyk op drie plaatzen beeſig, en door de Biſſchoppen van Keulen en Munſter geholpen, van alle kanten de oorlogsvyeren deed opgaan; ondertuſſen van meening zynde met twintig duyzend paarden, over den Rhyn; door Betuw en Veluw op Amſterdam te rukken, en in 't onderbrengen van die Stad, de doodſteek aan de Vereenigde Staat te geeven. 'T liep ook (wie kan 't klaar bewyzen) door vreemde ongevallen op 't hef, en zyn volk binnen Naarden, Muyden en Woerden.

Het onderloopen der Landen rondom Amſterdam, (welk ik *Voorbeeld om Amſterdam.* hier alleen tot voorbeeld neem) is viermaal in veertig jaren gebeurd, zo door inbraak van de te ſterk ingeſwolle zeegolven, als door de bekommering voor de aennaderende Vyand. Van deze doorbraken zyn de meeſte Hofſteden, zo in haare Gebouwen als Plantagien meeſt bedorven geworden; maar 't Zeewater uytgekeert zynde, zyn beyde Huyzen, en Plantagien niet alleen telkens beter, maar ook, als of dat quaad niet te kreunen was, tot dartele pragt en praal verheerlykt geworden.

De togten agter om na 't Waygats en de Straat Anian, de doorgeſtane folteringen van zulken achtmaandſe duiſterheyd en winter, zyn door dezer volkeren hardvochtigheyd gebraveert. En onvermoeyt de tornen hervat.

De neerlagen die zy in haare eerſte Zeeſlagen of Veldtogten in de Oorlogen ontfangen, zyn maar ſpooren om haar te prikkelen, weer ſterker telkens uyt te komen, tot dat zy de dreygende quaden ſtremmen, en de onderneemers tegen haar tot handſaamheyd kneeden.

Voor haar zelven in 't byzonder ziet menſe niet licht zoo *Winſiekte* vergenoegt datze uyt de winſten om de moeyten ſcheyden, maar of door gewoonte of door wat gierigheyd, willen zy liever ryker ſterven en armer leeven.

In geen Land, is het geld op minder renten, als by deze, wanneer voor 't wederkrygen, genoegſame veiligheyd is. En als

I. Deel.   B

Yes, they even made a benefit out of the heat of the battle, they stretched the boundaries far and wide, even to such an extent that they were forced, (which seldom happens) to make peace because of too much shrinking of the power of the enemy. But this was followed by the most terrible storm of France's raging lust for power. Her three armies, at the same time busy in three different places, and helped by the Bishops of Cologne and Munster, caused the flames of war to flare up again; meanwhile, with the intention to march upon Amsterdam with twenty thousand horses, crossing the Rhine and marching through the Betuwe and Veluwe and, in subjugating this city, to give the death-blow to the United Provinces. It came to nothing (as we can prove it clearly) through strange mishaps and through the people of Naarden, Muiden and Woerden.

The inundation of the land around Amsterdam (which I take here only as an example) happened four times in forty years, through the influx of too heavily swollen waves of the sea as well as from the fear of the approaching enemy. Most of the homesteads, their buildings and also their arable land have suffered by these floods. But after the withdrawal of the seawater both houses and land were not only better every time, but also, as if these disasters were heedless of anything, the houses and land were improved to gay splendour and magnificence.

The expeditions round the "Waygats" and the Anian Straits, the torments of such an eight months during darkness and winter have been defied by the hardiness of these people. And untiringly the exertion was resumed.

The defeats they suffered in their first naval battles or campaigns are only spurs to stimulate them to emerge stronger every time until they stop the threatening evils and mould their adversaries into manageability.

As, particularly for themselves, they do not look so satisfied as if they rather would do without profits than take all the trouble, but either from force of habit or out of some avarice, they would rather die rich and live poor.

In no other country does money bear less interest than here as long as there is enough security to get it back. And if that should happen, the abundance between wars, however, makes it so that to invest one's money one has to beseech rather than be beseeched. Thus foreign rulers also borrow big amounts, yes, even although the prohibition is very strict, much of the money is now put out at interest in France because of the allurement of a fair return, as it was previously in Spain.

The charges, however heavy they might be, were born with quiet obedience from force of habit and, letting their purses be their masters, seeing to it that the outgoings balance the receipts.

Jealousy is little known amongst these people because most men and women are rather cool and, not looking for loose living themselves, they do not easily suspect such wickedness in others. One sees many women of the common people marry and after living together for weeks or months, yes, even for only a few days, their husbands, hired for three, four, five or six years, going on expeditions to other regions, their chastity usually remaining without blot or scandal.

Politeness has already been more or less generally adopted by yound and old, but in North-Holland and Friesland the ordinary people consider compliments, bowing, courtly homage as the whims of a buffoon; they laugh at them and hate them. On the contrary, they are rough-mannered, but honest in dealing with money and business affairs, just as one can entrust workmen with anything except beer and wine.

Equality is a wonderful and attractive principle for the people in these provinces, whom it is difficult to submit (as long as they have not changed by long domination). Now the inhabitants here as elsewhere are submitted, but it does not appear to them as such, since the change of government and the positions often unesteemed people can obtain there, seems to flatter them, so that they do not have to despair. Apart from that fact there are many provinces and towns in which the guilds or court-martial, existing outside the authorities, seem to participate in the government of which they reckon themselves to be part.

Splendour of courtly style is, unlike honour in these countries

---

als dat ontſtaat zo maakt egter den overvloed in 't midden der Oorlogen, dat men om 't zyne uyt te zetten eer bidden moet als gebeeden werd ; zo dat ook vreemde Vorſten by deeze groote ſommen opneemen; ja zelf, hoe naauw de verboden gaan, veele gelden om het lokaas der ſware renten aan Spanjen eertyts, en nu nog aan Vrankryk uytgezet werden.

De laſten hoe zeer ze groot zyn werden door de gewoonte met ſtille gehoorzaamheyd gedragen, de teering na de neering, de ſpilling na 't inkomen werdende gereegeld.

Buyten Minyver.   Jalouzy is onder deze weynig bekent, om dat de meeſte Mans en Vrouwen vry koel zyn, en geen vry bejag zelfs zoekende, vermoedenſe ook niet ligt zulke boosheyd van een ander. Men ziet 'er veele Vrouwen onder 't gemeen volk trouwen, en na weeken of maanden bywooning, ja zelfs voor weynige dagen, de Mans van de Vrouwen voor drie, vier, vyf of zes jaaren verhuurd, togten na andere Geweſten doen, blyvende de kuysheyd meeſt zonder vlek of opſpraak.

Niet voor de Hoflyk-heyd.   Beleeftheyd is in eenige der zeeven Landen al vry heus en hoflyk onder grooten en kleynen, maar in Noordholland, en Vrieſland, acht het geringſte volk, de pligtpleegingen, buygingen, hoflyke eerbetuygingen, hansops grillen, lachtſe uyt, en haatſe. Zynde daar en teegen van ſtuurſe zeeden maar trouw in het behandelen van gelden en zaken, gelyk ook alle de werkluyden, die buyten wyn en bier, alles mag toevertrouwt werden.

De gelykheyd is in de gemeene beſten een wonderſchoon en aantrekkelyk middel voor de gemoederen, aan wien het onderwerpen (zo de luyden door lange verſlaaftheyd niet en zyn buyten natuurlyke ſmaak gebragt) laſtig is. Nu zyn de ingezeetenen hier zo wel als elders onderworpen, maar 't en komt *Waarom.* haar zo niet voor, daar de verandering der regeeringen, en het deel welk daar in vaak ongeachte luyden konnen krygen, haar ſchynt te vlyen, als of zy ook niet gantſch daar van te wanhopen hadden. Behalven dat 'er veele Provincien en Steeden zyn, in de welke de Gilden, of Krygsraad buyten de Overigheyt beſtäande een aandeel van 't beſtier ſchynt te heb-*Praal in kleedy.* ben, onder welk zy haar zelven reekenen.

Pragt van hoflyke ſtoet is ongelyk de eere deezer Landen,

meer

meer als d'anderen eygen. Daar zynder die de veelheyd van Dienftboden, Paarden en Rytuigen, als groote en voortreffelyke teekenen van welftand aanzien, maar in de befte Koopfteeden gelden de lieden minder in 't vertrouwen op de Beurs, na tegenwicht van zulke verquiftende Nachtgaften. En men reekent den menfche niet tot verdienften, 't geen zy door koften uytbrengen, maar 't geen zy door zuinigheyd in brengen. Van kleederen is het zelfde, namentlyk ligt te onderfcheyden of de Burgers digt aan Hoven, onder Eedelen of Krygsluy haar winften doen, dan of zy met Kooplieden omgaan, en van de zwier, en wild waayigheyd afkyken. In 't algemeen kan men zeggen, dat de rykfte in haar uyterlykheyd beminnen te hoo- *Niet geagt.* ren, dat zy onder haar ftaat gaan, en dat men op haar uytfchiet; zou men die Man wel aanzien, dat hy zulken magt heeft? yets van 't oude Hollands en Fries, met wat ingetogene dragt der Doopsgefinden, helpt te zamen veel tot die zeedige kleedingen en 't myden van fleep en ftoet op ftraat.

Maar de zelfde ingetoogentheyd vintmen geenfins in de *Pragt in Huysraden.* Huysraden, Thuynen en Hoffteeden: gemeene Schippers, Stuurluy, en minder Ambachtsluy, hebben Vrouwen, welke *Lywaat.* Kaffen houden gepropt van uytmuntend fijn Lywaat, alderuytgepiktfte Tafelgoed, Bedden, en lyfsbehoef, ja kiften met de geboorte der Kinderen al vol gepakt met zulken uitzetting, zoo overvloedig dat 'er zwaarlyk een Marquis in Vrankryk, zo goeden en zo veel Lywaat tot zyn en zyn Huysgefins beflag hout, als een gemeene Hollandfche Vrouw.

Porcelynen zyn in zulken overvloed, de oude en befte Kraak- *Porcelynen:* porcelynen zo wel als minder foorten, dat de vreemdeling verbafen moet zulks te zien.

Schilderyen, en Teekenkonft, by na in alle de Huyfen tot *Schilderyen.* verwondering veel, en by aanzienlyke, oude en voortreffelyke ftukken. Boeken, zo veel by Borgers en zo net en pragtig gebonden, dat men 'er in getal niet meer by een Hoog Schoolleeraar behoefden te eyffchen.

Fluweelen, niet zo algemeyn nog pragtig als by andere. Silverwerk, voor Tafel en dienft, Thee en Koffy zeer gemeen. Koper en Tin, en allerley Huysraad brand fchoon en overvloedig. Bloemen, tot Dolheyd toe, in prys en uytlachens waar- *Bloemen.* dig

---

more peculiar to some people than to others. There are people who consider the amount of servants, horses and carriages as great and excellent signs of prosperity, but in the best commercial towns those people enjoy less esteem at the exchange after the counter-balance of such extravagant fly-by-nights. And one does not give people credit for what they spend but for what they gain by economy. The same applies to clothes, for it is easy to see whether the burghers carry on trade close to the courts or amongst noblemen or warriors or whether they associate with merchants and then dress less elegantly and courtly. Generally it can be said that the rich like to hear that their appearance is beneath their station and that one is deceived, and asks, does that man appear so powerful? Something of the old Dutch and Frisian and also the austere attire of the Mennonites contributes to modesty in fashion and avoidance of train and retinue in the streets.

But the same modesty is not at all to be found in the households, gardens and farmsteads; ordinary skippers, helmsmen and the lesser artisans have wives who have wardrobes crammed with the finest linen, the most exquisite table-linen, bed- and body-linen, yes, at the birth of their children they already have chests fully packed with such outfits, so plentiful that in France there is hardly a marquis who has such good and so much linen in stock for himself and his family as an ordinary Dutch housewife. There is porcelain in such abundance, the ancient and best egg-shell china as well as the cheaper kinds, that the foreigner must be surprised to see all this.

There are an amazing amount of paintings and drawings in almost every house and in those of people of high rank old and excellent pieces. At the burghers' there are so many books, neatly and beautifully bound, that one would not expect a greater amount at a professor's.

Velvets are not quite so general yet, but as beautiful as elsewhere. Silver for table and service, tea and coffee are also very general. Brass and pewter and all sorts of household effects are spotlessly clean and abundant. Flowers are expensive without all sense of proportion and deserving of derision because of the ardour great men evince for these things.

Orangeries, foreign plants, collections of curiosities are found more in one town than in whole kingdoms elsewhere.

Amazing is the boldness and the readiness in trade. In Holland, especially in Amsterdam or Rotterdam, one often sees, during the week, the auction of the Dutch East India Company and at the same time two or three loadings of ships from Smyrna or from the West Indies to the amount of seven and eight million, all manned within eight or ten days and usually written off at the discount bank.

However big the morsel, they set themselves to chew it, business never being checked because of the large amount of money involved.

Although in many matters their firmness can be perceived, it cannot be denied that these people are very quickly excited by good news and have a special weakness for easily believing what they want to believe, but on the other hand they also are extremely disheartened by the first onset of misfortune. However all together they are very impatient with twaddling generals and admirals. It seems that not doing things pleases them as little as doing things badly. Conceited as they are they sooner believe that there is betrayal in the affairs than that they have failed in courage or temerity.

The difference of these lands is very peculiar; the glory of other countries lies in external flag-showing, here it is in the way of modest and thrifty house-keeping, elsewhere it is deemed an honour not to esteem money, to squander it on theatrical enjoyment and beautiful performances. There it is ample payment with long credit without criticism, here on the other hand it is in not having debts, not to borrow, paying cash, close bargaining, making a point of a penny change, skimping and keeping an eye on everything down to the smallest coins. But however accurately one may skimp, avoiding to be called a quarreller or niggling wrangler, revenging derision by fist or sword as if it had been done to women, is not worth as good a name here as, in patience, checking other people's temper with good words. Likewise punishment for slander is almost out of practice in Holland. One does not hear of physical fights here. Good governing has helped civil murder out of existence. And although with the laying up of the fleet there are a lot of

---

dig den yver die groote Mannen in die dingen toonen.

Oranjery, vreemde gewaffen, Cabinetten van Rariteyten, meer in eene Stad , als in gantfche Koninkryken elders.

Wonderlyk is haare ftoutheyd en gereetheyd in 't Koopman-fchappen : men ziet in Holland byzonder in Amfterdam of Rotterdam, op een week, dikmaals de verkooping der Ooftindi-fche Maatfchappy, en te gelyk twee of drie ladingen van Sche-pen van Smirna of uit de Weft-Indien aangeleyd , tot zeven en acht millioenen, in acht of thien dagen alles gemant, en in de Wiffel-Bank meeft afgefchreeven.

Hoe groot de brok is men zet 'er de mont na, nimmer ftuy-ten de zaken om de veelheyd van geld, dat 'er aan hangt.

Driftig tot wat nieuws. Hoe veelmen in veele zaken werd gewaar hare ftandvaftig-heyd, zo kan men echter niet ontkennen, dat alle deeze Vol-keren, zeer fchielyk opfwellen van goede tydingen, en byzon-der een zwakheyd hebben ligt te gelooven 't geen fe begeeren, maar ook daar en teegen, byfter neergeflagen in de eerfte aan-ftoot der ongelukken: zamen evenwel zeer ongeduldig tegen Veldoverftens of Zeevoogden, die ze zien leuteren, 't fchynt dat niet doen haar min als qualyk doen behaagt. Waan van haar zelven hebbende, gelovenfe eerder dat 'er verradery in de za-ken is , als dat zy in moed of ftoutheyd te kort gefchooten zyn.

Verfchil der Landen. Dezer Landen verfchil is zeer zonderling ; de glorie in andere Landen is in uyterlyke Vlaggen gelegen , hier is de manier van zedig en zuynig Huyshouden , elders is 'er een eer in geleegen geld niet te achten , te fpillen in batementen plaifieren, heerlyke toeftel ; ruyme betaling fonder opmer-king met lang borgen, daar en tegen hier in geen fchulden te heb-ben, niet te borgen, Contant af betalen, naau dingen, op een quart-jen in Wiffel-geld ftaan, tot de geringfte octaafjens alles na te gaan en uyt te ziften. Maar hoe naauw men ziften mag , de naam van querellier of krabbel Krakeelder te myden, hoon met vuyft of deegen te wreeken, al was 't Vrouwen aangedaan, is hier zo goede naam niet waard , als laf in gedult, anderen hun drift af te ftuyten met goede woorden; ook is in Holland fchier buyten practyk, de ftraf van Laftering. Van Lyf gevegten hoort men hier niet. Het goed beftier heeft die borgermoord uyt de weg geholpen. En fchoont 'er by 't opleggen der Vlooten

grim-

grimmeld van los en ligtveerdig Zeevolk, langs de Straten, in de Steeden van Holland, Zeeland, en Vriefland, vind men nochtans feer felden groote wanorders uyt haar fpooreloosheyd, zo vlug is de fterke hand der Juftitie, achter de misdaders. 't Ganfche Land is veylig van Struykrovers, Bofchmoorders; van Swartmakers, heeft men meer gefchreeuwt, als gevoeld, en fulken quaad is niet heel te ontgaan, by 't afdanken van het overtollig Krygsvolk.

Doch de inwoonders zetten hun in 't kort na de Oorlogen tot hervatten van hunne handwerken, en 't Land bouwen, en de uytheemfen raken of aan diergelyke middelen, hier neer gezet, of zoeken hare gelukken, op de tochten naar Ooft of Weft-Indien.

In Holland leeft men van 't water, in Gelderland van 't land; gelyk heeft in Gelderland zyn eygen Vrugten, Veldgewas en inkomen: maar in Holland moet zulks al van andere Landen en andere Menfchen en van buyten ingebracht werden. Hier zyn de Kerken ongeciert, maar de Borgershuyzen prachtig, en in de andere landen, de borgers huyzen arm en de Kerken ryk. De inkomens der geeftelyken doen al het vette der aarden in hare Schotel komen, en de reft der Menfchen leeft behoeftig, maar hier is alles contrarie. Hier is de Koopman hoog geacht, daar den Edelman.

De rykdom van veele Landen en vafte goederen te hebben, is in Holland niet hoog gewaardeerd, maar in tegendeel geen andere in naam by de Stichtenaars, Gelderze en Overyffelers, en byzonder by de Vriezen en Groningers, alwaar de goederen meeft dragen de macht van ftemmen; ja eenige zoo alleen uyt hare eygene achtb aarheyd tot 's Lands of Staats vergadering haar bezitters zenden, waarom ze ook op zeer goede pryzen blyven, daar men in Noord-Holland, verfchriklyk verval, door 's Lands laften, in de Oorlogen, in de Landen en vafte Goederen gezien heeft.

Deze byzondere verfcheydenheyd der gronden van welftand in de zeven Volkeren, veroorzaakt daarom te lichter de lange leutering in de fware raadsbefluyten. Zeeland ter kaap gewoon toe te ruften, en zulken winft voor een hoofd neering houdende, heeft byna tegen alle Vredefluytingen geprotefteerd. Holland-

Onderfchid der geftelte niffe in de Landen.

Oorfaak der Verwylingen.

---

loose and reckless sailors along the streets in the cities of Holland, Zeeland and Friesland one nevertheless very rarely sees wild disorder as a result of their indiscipline so quickly does the strong arm of justice catch up with the evil-doers. The whole country is safe from highwaymen and brigands. Of blackguards more has been heard about than experienced and this kind of evil cannot entirely be escaped by the discharge of redundant soldiers.

But the inhabitants made them restart their trades and farming shortly after the wars and the foreigners either get settled by these means or they go in search of adventure on expeditions to the East or West Indies.

In Holland one lives of the water, in Guelderland of the land; so Guelderland has its own fruit, produce of the fields and income. But in Holland all that has to be brought in from other countries, by other people and from outside. Here the churches are simple, but the houses of the burghers are beautiful; in other countries the houses are poor and the churches are rich. The revenues of the clergy make them live on the fat of the land while the rest of the people live in need. Here however everything is the other way round; here the merchant is highly honoured, elsewhere the nobleman.

Having landed property and real estate is not highly appreciated in Holland. But on the contrary it is different in value with the people of the bishopric of Utrecht, the Guelders and the people of Overyssel and particularly with those of Friesland and Groningen, where the estates have the right to vote. Yes, only on account of their own respectability some of them send their proprietors to the meeting of the States General. That is the reason why they keep their very good value, since in North Holland one has seen a terrible decline in land and real estate as a result of the rates and taxes of the province during the wars. This particular difference in reasons for prosperity in the seven provinces therefore more easily causes the long dawdling in difficult decisions. Zeeland, accustomed to equip for privateering and considering this kind of profits as a main trade, has protested against almost all peace-treaties.

Holland, full of mercantile and manufacturing towns, industrious in large and small fisheries, has almost always pushed the peace negotiations too much, yes, even so much that the enemies are used to rely on it.

Increasing armies, keeping the men prepared is desired by Guelderland, the bishopric of Utrecht, Overyssel and others because their brave nature looks for prosperity in military functions. Holland and Zeeland always insist on withdrawal of those forces, on giving furlough, discharging or decreasing the land forces and nullifying important functions. Holland will take the prohibition of French goods seriously and so will others, but still others on the contrary connive at the import because of the profits.

Yes, one town has a considerable interest in taxing or prohibiting foreign cloths, be it woollen, silk, cotton or linen, while another town is for free trade and import of the same.

These differences were almost always settled by mutual agreement and did not result in an obstinate breaking away from the bond of towns in any province, not in a breach between two provinces and thus in a severance of the sworn Union. Which union makes and maintains the whole force of each province and the continual power of the commonwealth. Through this they have become great, each in particular and all in general. Their minted coin for the States General of the Seven Provinces shows a crowned lion, holding a sheaf of seven arrows firmly bound and also a broad-sword to defend and protect those united arrows and this device or circumscription.

Concordia res parvae crescunt

More details will appear to us more clearly when each of the provinces is dealt with, for which reason wo do not have to go into all the virtues and failings, gifts and qualities of the inhabitants now.

---

land met Koop en Werkfteeden vervult, op de groote en kleyne Viffchery yverig, heeft meeft altyd de Vreedens handelingen te fterk aangezet, ja zo zeer, dat 'er de Vyanden, op gewoon zyn ftaat te maken.

*En ver-
fchillende
belangen.*

Legers te vergrooten, de Manfchap op de been te houden, ziet men van Gelderland, het Sticht, Overyffel en andere begeeren, om dat hare brave Landaerd in de Krygsampten haar welvaren zoeken. Holland en Zeeland, ftaan altyd op de intrekking van die Machten, het verlof geeven, afdanken of onderfteeken der Lands machten, en 't vernietigen der fware Ampten. Holland zal ernftig vallen op een verbod van Franze waren; ook andere, maar andere daar en teegen, zien, om de winften, den invoer door de vingeren.

Ja de eene ftad heeft tegen den anderen zo aanmerkelyk belang tot befwaring of verbod der uytheemze ftoffen, 't zy van Wollen, Syden, Catoen of Linnen, als de andere voor de vryen handel en invoer der zelven.

*Door over-
reeding
weer te ef-
fenen.*

Welke verfcheyden echter by na altyd in der minnen werden gematigt, en niet en komen tot ftyfhoofdige barft tegen de band der Steeden in yder Provincie, noch ook van de eene der Provincien tegen den andere, tot een verbreekinge der zamen gefwoorene Unie. Welke Eendragt de gantfe kracht van yder Land, en de geduyrende Macht van Haar Algemeyn Beft maakt en behoud. Door dezelve zyn zy, elk in 't byzonder, en te zamen groot geworden. Volgens haar geflagen penning, vertoonende voor de Generaliteyt der zelver zeeven Landen, een Leeuw gekroond, houdende de bondel der zeeven pylen wel verknocht by een, en daar by een houwer om die vereenigde pylen wel te verdeedigen en befchermen, met dit devys of omfchrift.

Concordia res parvæ Crefcunt.

Door Eendragt werden kleyne zaken groot.

Meerder byzonderheeden zullen ons klaarder in 't behandelen van elke Provincie voorkomen, weshalven wy tot nader ziften van de inwoonders gebreeken, deugden, gaven en hoedanigheeden, nu niet behoeven te rucken.

Wy

Wy zyn wel van meynig niet de aandagt der Leſer met oude zaken op te houden, doch de zaak welke wy verhandelen, eyſcht dat men een wynig aanraakt de laaſt verloopene ten min- ſten twee of drie eeuwen: om dat in die van 1400 tot 1500. de Landen in de groote ongelegentheeden der burgerlyke Oorlo- gen, zeer licht op haaren hals kreegen, Stadhouders, die als 'er maar een glimp was, verbranden deze of geene ſtad en ver- klaarden de zelve vervallen van alle hare Privilegien. Om haar de handen te laten vullen met het nieuw afgeperſte geld tot het herſtellen der oude gerechtigheeden, of het ſchenken van nieu- we rechten, zo in het bevoordeelen en octroyeeren van zom- mige inkomens, of behouden van vryheeden, op havens of ri- vieren, ſtapelrechten, of merkten; of in het maken of verkie- zen van hare rechters of regeerders. Machten der Gilden, Krygsraden, en andere Broederſchappen.

En om dat in de Eeuw van 1500 tot 1600 de Landen van Bourgondien aan Caſtilien quamen, en die Caſtiliaanzen of Spaanzen Koning haar Hertog, Graaf of Heer, (want die had alle de zeventien onder zyn geweld) misbruykende zyn bepaal- de magt, wierd afgeſwooren, en tuſſen zeeven der zelver Lan- den een eeuwig duurend Verbond geſlooten, zynde de Unie van Uytrecht; waar door een zeer groot onderſcheyd der zaaken ontſtond, van welke eenige weg raakten en andere bleeven; maar byzonderlyk om dat binnen de Eeuw van 1600 tot 1700. door de Af en Aanzetting van het Stadhouderſchap in vyf der- zelve vereenigde Landen, eenige veranderingen gebracht zyn in eenige zaken, welke zommige ook nu blyven en andere weg- genomen zyn.

Dit kort verhaal dan van die Eeuwen zullen wy doen door- gaan tot op de Unie van Uytrecht: en daar mede het Hiſto- rize meeſt voldaan reekenen, als zynde niet van ons oogwit, als voor zo verre het de zaken van Landen of Steeden beſtier geraakt heeft of veranderd.

TWEE

Our opinion is that we should not hold up the attention of the reader by ancient affairs, but the affair we deal with requires of us that we touch slightly upon at least two or three centuries because in the one between 1400 and 1500 the provinces, during the great difficulties of the civil wars, were easily ruined. Stadtholders burned down one or another town and excluded it from all its privileges at the slightest provocation to fill their own pockets by the extortion of money for reinstating the old rights or presenting new ones, as well as for granting privileges and charters for some revenues or for the retaining of immunity in harbours and on rivers, staple-rights, or markets. They give the right to appoint or chose their judges or rulers and also power to the guilds, courts-martial and other fraternities.

And because in the century between 1500 and 1600 the lands of Burgundy fell to Castile and the Castilian or Spanish king, duke, count or lord (for it was he who had all the seventeen regions in his power), abusing this power, was abjured and a perpetual union was concluded between seven of those provinces. This Union of Utrecht resulted in a great diversity of matters, some of which disappeared and others remained, but particularly because within the century between 1600 and 1700 in esta- blishing and abolishing the stadtholdership in five of those united provinces some changes have been made in several matters of which some still exist and others have been removed. Thus this short history of those centuries we shall continue up to the Union of Utrecht and therewith consider the historical aspect sufficient for the greater part, it not being our purpose as far as it has touched or altered the affairs of the ruling of the provinces and towns.

RUSTIC SCENES

Shepherd with cow, two goats and a sheep

Shepherdess carrying a flower basket

Two scenes with cattle

Two-wheeled carriage on a high road

Feast of the solstice – two prints

A sportsman (hunter) and an angler

Reference: H   F. W. H. Hollstein. *Dutch and Flemish Etchings. Engravings and Woodcuts.*
Volume IX. Amsterdam 1953

H 349   R. de Hooghe, no address   12.2 × 13 cm

H 346   Hooghe 1662, no address   9.2 × 12.5 cm

H 153   not signed, after N. Berchem   9.1 × 12.1 cm

H 152   not signed, after N. Berchem   9.2 × 12.2 cm

TWO-WHEELED CARRIAGE ON A HIGH ROAD

I H 354   R. Hooge fec et inv.   12 × 15.6 cm
II H 354   R. Hooge inv. et fecit-, plate reduced: 10.3 × 15.8 cm

H 355   R. de Hooghe fec et inv., no address   c. 11 × 15.6 cm

H 356   R. de Hooge fec. et inv., no address   c. 10 × 15.5 cm

H 375   not signed, no address   11 × 16 cm

PLATES ARBITRARILY

ATTRIBUTED TO DE HOOGHE

H 351-352   Two scenes after Philip Wouwerman

H 353   Two soldiers at the bank of a river

H 357   Horseman and groom

H 358   Horseman at the ford

NEWSPRINTS

References: H F. W. H. Hollstein. *Dutch and Flemish Etchings. Engravings and Woodcuts.*

Volume IX. Amsterdam 1953

FM F. Muller. *De Nederlandsche geschiedenis in platen.*

Amsterdam 1863-1882. 4 vols. (Reprint: Amsterdam 1970)

vSt G. van Rijn. *Atlas van Stolk.*

Amsterdam, 's-Gravenhage 1895-1931. 10 vols. *Index.* 's-Gravenhage 1933

LA J. Landwehr. *Romeyn de Hooghe* (1645-1708) *as book illustrator. A bibliography.*

Amsterdam, New York 1970.

NEWSPRINTS

1667 Rochester and marine base – The isle Shepey and the fortress Sheerness, England, attacked by the Dutch under Admiral de Ruyter

Peace conference and ratification at Breda, Holland *(two versions)*

1668 The Dauphin baptised in St. Germain en Laye, France

1669 Victory of Cornelis Speelman over the Kingdom of Macassar and the war from 1666 till 1669

1672 Prince Willem III sworn in commander-in-chief over the Forces in the Republic

Prince Willem III entry into Amsterdam – see Portraits p. 257

Siege of Groningen by the Elector of Cologne and the Bishop of Munster – see also LA 37/41

Johan and Cornelis de Witt assaulted and murdered at The Hague *(two versions)* – see also LA 26/41/47/101 and under Portraits p. 263

Witten Wonder Spiegel – The exploits of the brothers de Witt

Spiegel der France Tirannye – The French army under the command of the Duke of Luxemburg terrorizing Zwammerdam and Bodegraven – see also LA 30-34

Johan Sikkinga recovering Coevorden and its Castle from the Bishop of Munster – see also LA 37/41

1673 Reduction of Nieuwe Schans by Karel Rabenhaupt

Three victorious sea-battles under de Ruyter over the English and French fleets – see also LA 41

The first and second sea-battle of the English and Dutch fleets

The third sea-battle of the English and Dutch fleets

Siege and reduction of Naarden by Willem III *(two versions)* – see also LA 41

A dike bursting near Coevorden – see also LA 41

Fortifications of the Castle Choczim on the Niester. Sobieski defeating the Turks

Siege and relief of the Castle Trembowla. Sobieski defeating the Turks

John Sobieski and map of Poland (three leaves)

Willem III capturing Bonn, Breuil and Rynbach – see also LA 8/41

1674 Prince Wilhelm of Fürstenberg arrested – see Political Caricatures p. 210

The events since war broke out in 1672 till February 1674

Peace negociated between England and the Republic in London

The Province of Utrecht rejoining the Union of Provinces

Coronation of John III of Poland in Cracow

The allied troops under Willem III and the French troops under Condé battling near Seneffe, Belgium – see also LA 41

Willem III besieging and capturing Grave *(three versions)*

The French attacking and withdrawing from Grave

Allegory on the victory in 1674 and Peace concluded

Allegory on the exploits of Willem III

1675	The titular duchy of Gelre and Zutphen offered to Willem III
	Victory of Frederick William Elector of Brandenburg over the Swedes near Fehrbelin
	Battle between Turenne and Montecuculi near Aschaffenburg, Germany
	Siege and conquest of Wismar by Christian IV of Denmark
	All Saints' Flood in the Republic
	Death and funeral of Amalia van Solms in Delft (two leaves)
	Orangien Wonderspiegel – Life and exploits of Willem III
1676	Charles V of Lorraine, Henry von Baden-Durlach etc. capturing
	Philipsburg, Germany – see also LA 8
	The allied Danish and Dutch seaforces under C. Tromp conquering the Swedish Fleet
	Siege of Maastricht by Prince Willem III and Count van Horn
	Funeral procession of fieldmarshal Paulus Wirtz in Amsterdam
	Capture of Christianstadt by Christian IV of Denmark
	Vorstelyck Tafereel – The state of affairs in Europe and the allied princes
	Balance van den Franse oorlog – Allegory of France and her allies at war
	Allegory on the exploits of Willem III
	Kayserlicher Triumphkalender
1677	Helsingborg recovered by the Swedish
	Admiral d'Estrees and Commander Binkes battling near the isle of Tobago, West Indies
	Funeral procession of Admiral de Ruyter in Amsterdam
	Capture of Stettin by Frederick William Elector of Brandenburg
	Capture of Marstrand and Carlsteen by General Gyldenloeve (two plates)
	Allegory on the marriage of Willem III to Mary Stuart and the wedding ceremony in London
	Allegory on the exploits of Willem III
1678	Campaign of Christian IV of Denmark on the isle of Rügen (two leaves)
	Count Stanislaus Potocki's misfortune near Mechlin, Belgium
	Willem III and Duke Villahermosa battling with the Count of Luxemburg near St. Denis, Hainaut
	Allegory on the Peace of Nijmegen and other events
	Allegory on the conclusion of the Peace of Nijmegen
1680	Allegory of the events of the year 1680
1683	Kara Mustapha besieging Vienna – see also LA 60/82
1684	Luxemburg bombarded by Marshal de Crequi
1685	Carlos II descending his coach *in:* D. Papebrochius. *Conatus chronico-historicus.* Antwerp 1685
	Aux armes, Gens de Dieu
	Persecution of the Protestants in France – see also p. 188
	Glorification of John III of Poland (four leaves)

NEWSPRINTS

1686	Siege (and relief) of Buda, Hungary
	Nauplia, Greece, conquered on the Turks by the Venetians
	Leopold I of Austria entry into Brussels after defeating the Turks in Buda (nine leaves)
	Victory of Charles V of Lorraine and Margrave Louis of Baden-Baden over the Turks near Nagyharsány, Hungary
1687	Allegory on Leopold I of Austria and Joseph
	Koning-Spel Courant op 't Jaer 1687
	Belgrad taken by storm by Maximilian Emanuel Elector of Bavaria
	Willem III setting sail for England from the marine base Hellevoetsluis – see LA 76
1688	Willem III setting sail and his arrival in Brixham or Torbay, England *(two versions)*
	Reception and entry of Willem III into London
	Arrival of Willem III in England etc.
	Restoration of the true religion and James II of England fleeing to Paris
1689	Reception of the Princess of Orange as Queen of England
	Coronation of Willem III and Mary Stuart in Westminster Abbey *(three versions)*
	Fireworks in London, Leiden, Maastricht, Amsterdam, The Hague, Hamburg, Bois-le-Duc, Haarlem
	Session of the House of Lords and the House of Commons with Willem III on the throne
	Allegory of Willem III being crowned King of England – see p. 260
	Londonderry, Ireland; the siege of Bonn, Germany
	Battle between the Prince of Waldeck and Marshal de Humieres near Walcourt, Belgium
	Allegory on the events in the year 1689
1690	Coronation of Joseph I of Hungary in Augsburg
	Victory of Willem III over the united Irish and French troops on the Boyne, Ireland (three leaves)
	James II of England fleeing to Paris
	Sea-battle near Bevesier or Beachy Head, England, see page 200
1691	Willem III entry into The Hague – see LA 79 and LA 80
	Victory of Louis Margrave of Baden-Baden over the Turks in Slankamen, Hungary
	Siege of Athlone, Ireland, see page 200
1692	Sea-battle between the allied and English and French Fleets near Cape La Hogue, France
	The French defeated by the Dutch and English fleets
	The allied forces against the French near Steenkerken, Belgium
1693	Willem III and the Duke of Luxemburg battling near Landen, Belgium, see page 200
1695	Death and funeral of Mary Queen of England in London (thirteen leaves)
	Willem III and his fleet near Dunkirk, France
	Namur besieged and captured by Willem III and Menno van Coehoorn

1695	The French garrison leaving Namur, Belgium
1697	Allegory on the peace-treaty at Rijswijk, see page 200
	Glorification of the victory on the Turks by Eugene of Savoye near Zenta, Hungary
1699	Persecution of the Protestants in France 1685 till 1699 – see also page 128
1700	Charles XII of Sweden blockading the Russian army near Narva
	Entry of Louis XIV into Dunkirk (two leaves)
1702	Haarlem mourning Willem III death in London
	Victory of the allied forces over France and Spain near Luzara
	Satire on the events in 1702 – see Political Caricatures p. 229
1704	Victory over the French by John Churchill Duke of Marlborough and Eugene of Savoye near Hochstedt and Blenheim, Bavaria *(four versions)*
	Victories over the French in the year 1704
1705	Barcelona captured

Afbeeldingh van de STADT en REVIER van ROCHESTER, CHETHAM, etc.

Het Eylandt Shepey en 't Fort SSirenasse

ROCHESTER AND MARINE BASE – THE ISLE SHEPEY AND THE FORTRESS SHEERNESS, ENGLAND, ATTACKED BY THE DUTCH UNDER ADMIRAL DE RUYTER – JUNE 19th TO JUNE 23rd 1667

I : vSt2358 FM2256a H76 W. Schellinks / R. de Hooge, address N. Visscher   37.5 × 51.3 cm
II: FM2256c without address

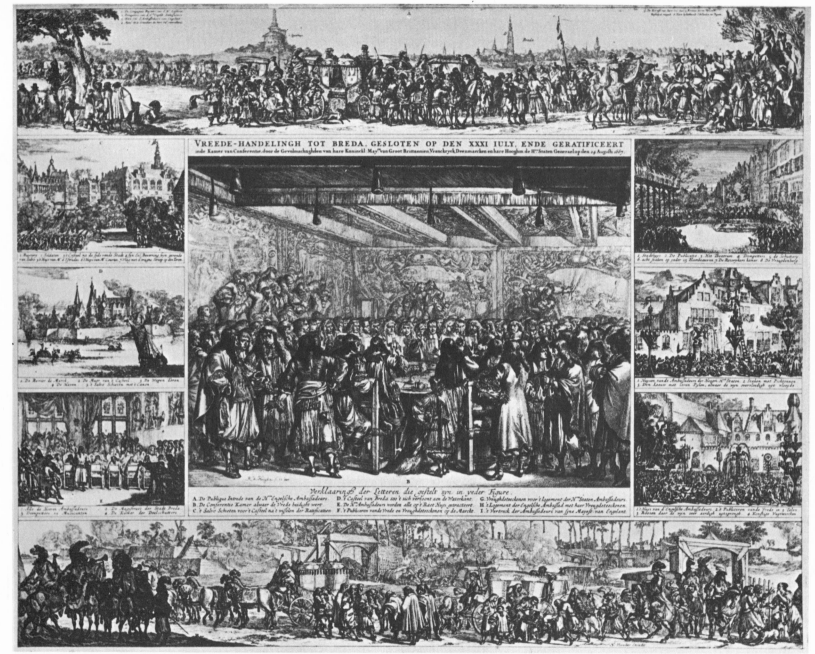

Ia : FM2284c H77 R. de Hooghe, before the letter and
inscription but with the heading   42 × 54.2 cm
Ib : Albertina Vienna has the same with German text
added
II : vSt2376 FM2284a H77 R. de Hooghe f. et inv.,
address N. Visscher
III: FM2284b with the address of J. Ottens (1663-1719)

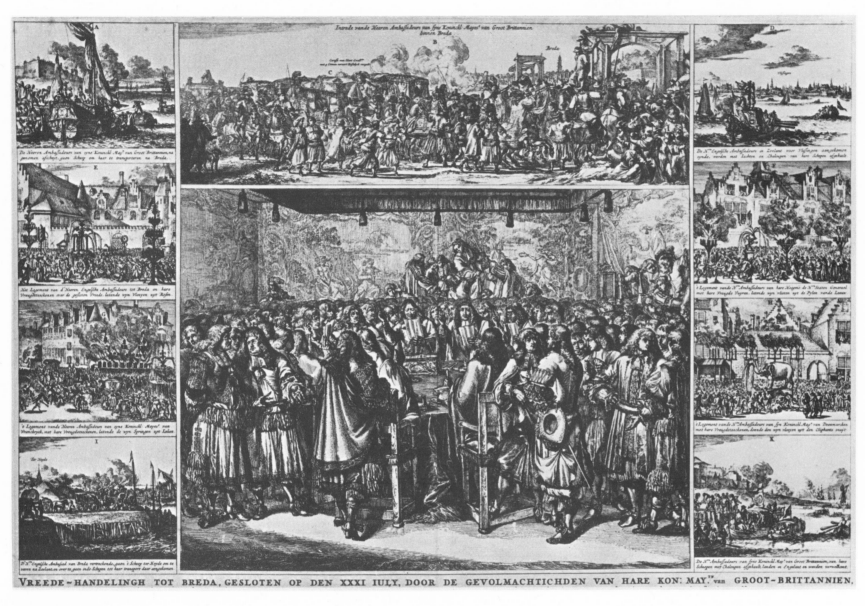

VREEDE~HANDELINGH TOT BREDA, GESLOTEN OP DEN XXXI IULY, DOOR DE GEVOLMACHTICHDEN VAN HARE KON: MAY.^{TE} van GROOT~BRITTANNIEN.

I : vSt2377 FM2285a H78 not signed, address
   N. Visscher on text-leaf   34.5 × 55 cm
II: FM2285b not signed, address J. Ottens
   (1663-1719)

THE DAUPHIN BAPTISED IN ST. GERMAIN EN
LAYE – MARCH 24th 1668

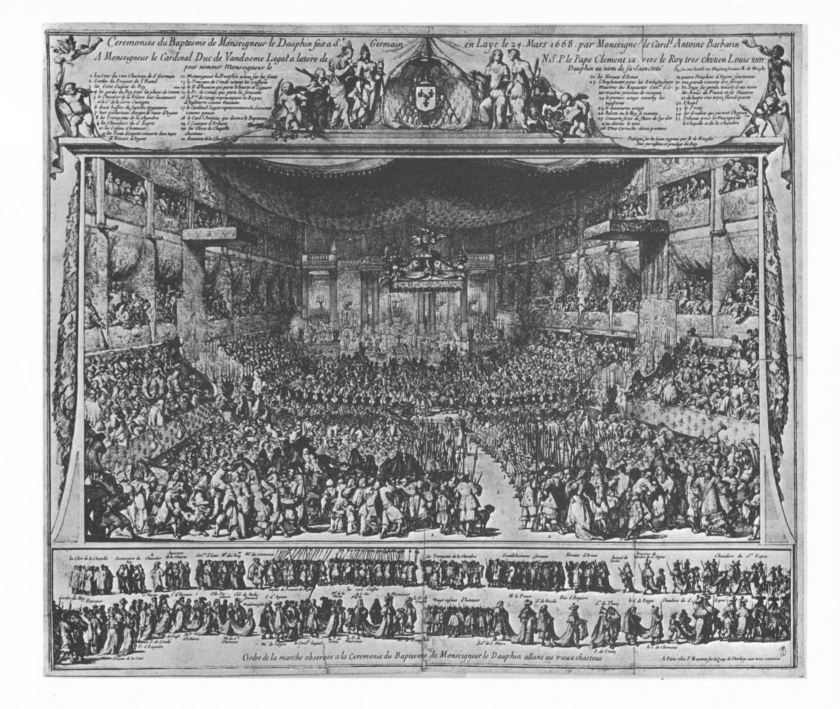

Museum Boymans-Van Beuningen. H80 Dessigné sur les
lieux et gravé par R. de Hooghe, address Paris chez
F. D. Lapointe   42.5 × 55.6 cm

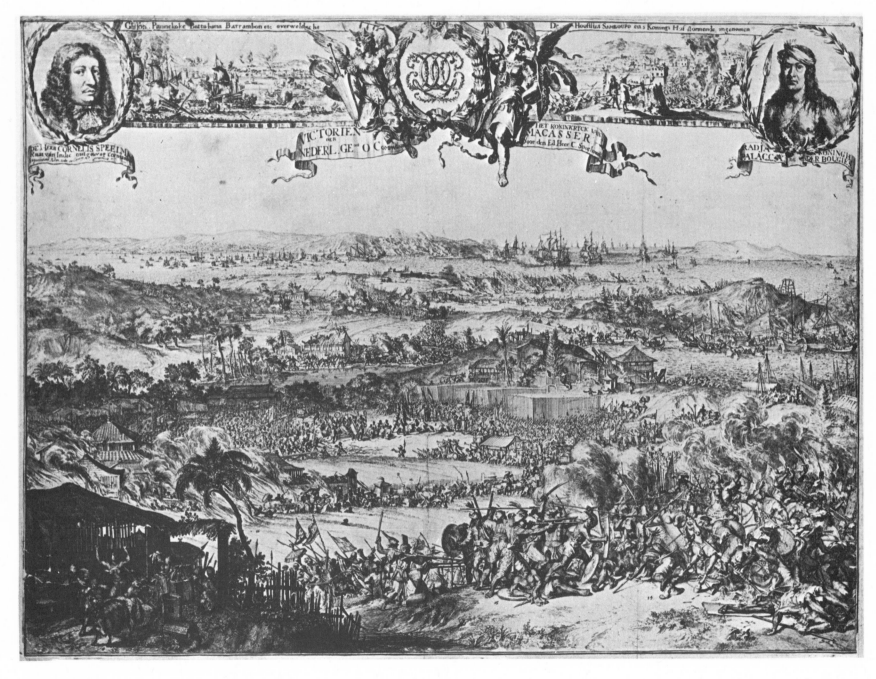

VICTORY OF CORNELIS SPEELMAN
OVER THE KINGDOM OF MACASSAR
AND RADJAH PALACCA, AND THE
WAR OF 1666 until 1669

I : FM2294A caption in five lines: "Victorie
der Macassaren..." and medallion portrait
of Cornelis Speelman – Teyler Museum,
Haarlem   39 × 54.5 cm

II: vSt2391 FM2294 H81 as reproduced with
six-line poem by Vondel and dedication by
De Hooghe

PRINCE WILLEM III SWORN IN COMMANDER-
IN-CHIEF OVER THE FORCES IN THE REPU-
BLIC-FEBRUARY 25th 1672

I : vSt2410 H84 not signed, address M. Doornick
     Amsterdam   26.8 × 31.8 cm
II : FM2316 signed R. de Hooghe f et inv
III: in *Hollandsche Mercurius* Haarlem, 1674 ⊥A8
IV: A copy with the date "10 July 1672" in Van Domse-
     laar. *Het Ontroerde Nederlandt,* 1676

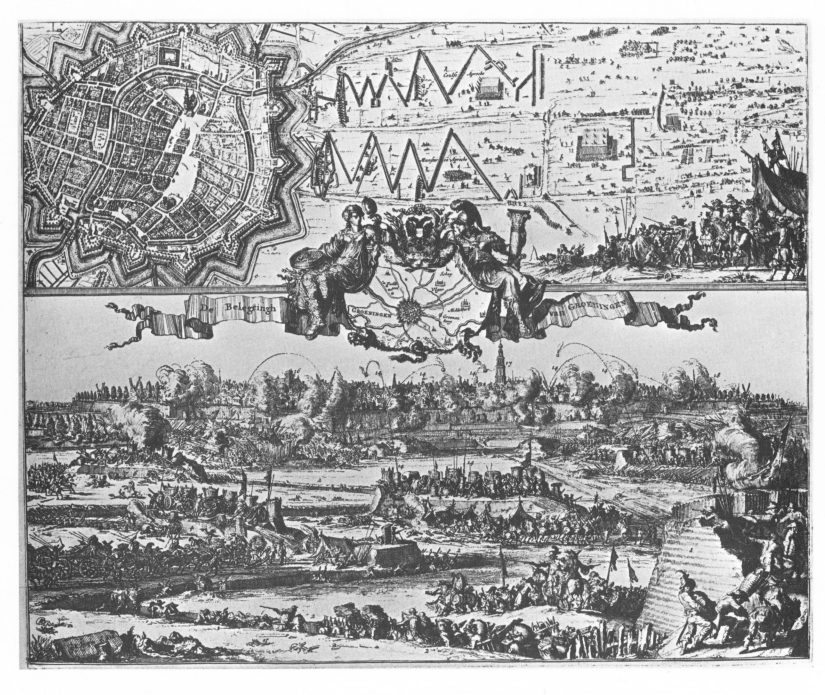

Ia: vSt2444 FM2383a H85 R. de Hooghe f. 1672, no
    address   31 × 40 cm
Ib: in *Het Ontroerde Nederlandt*, Amsterdam 1674 –
    LA37

JOHAN AND CORNELIS DE WITT ASSAULTED
AND MURDERED AT THE HAGUE – AUGUST
20th 1672

Ia: vSt2453 FM2401a + supp. H87 all scenes signed
    R. de Hooghe, no address   31.2 × 40.2 cm
Ib: in *Het Ontroerde Nederlandt*, Amsterdam 1674 (not
    signed) – LA37
II: vSt2454 not signed, address Carel Allard Amsterdam
    (1647-1706)

Ia: vSt2456 FM2403a H88 with Dutch text, Romijn
    de Hooghe des. et sc. 1672   32 × 42.7 cm
Ib: The same but with Dutch and French text
II : with the address of Carel Allard Amsterdam (1647-
    1706)

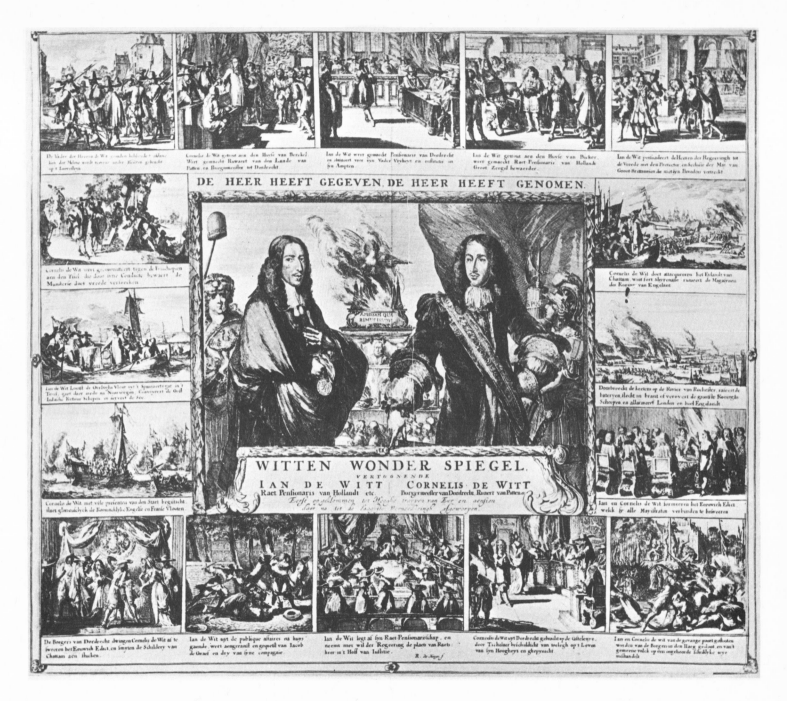

I : vSt2478 FM2390 H86 R. de Hooghe f. and with his
address   46.2 × 56 cm
II: FM2390b The same signature, address J. de Ram
Amsterdam

Spiegel der
FRANCE TIRANNYE
oepleecke opde Nollantsche Dorpen.

Romyn de Hooghe fec. 1673

Ia: vSt2489 FM2435 H89 Romyn de Hooghe fec. 1673,
   no address   31 × 39 cm
Ib: in *Het Ontroerde Nederlandt*, Amsterdam 1674 –
   LA37

Ia: vSt2496 FM2445 not signed, no address
    17 × 28 cm
Ib: in *Het Ontroerde Nederlandt*, Amsterdam
    1674 – LA37

vSt2526 FM2477 + supp. not signed, address H. Sweerts,
Amsterdam   23.5 × 23.2 cm

VICTORIOUS SEA-BATTLES UNDER ADMIRAL
DE RUYTER OVER THE ENGLISH AND FRENCH
FLEETS: NEAR SCHOONEVELD JUNE 7th and
14th; NEAR KIJKDUIN AUGUST 21st 1673

I : vSt2533 FM2462 + supp. not signed, text with address
    H. Sweerts, Amsterdam   42.2 × 51.2 cm
II: FM3359 adapted for the sea-battle near Malaga, Spain,
    August 24th 1704 with the portraits erased and the
    cartouches altered

THE FIRST AND SECOND SEA-BATTLE OF THE
ENGLISH AND DUTCH FLEETS NEAR SCHOO-
NEVELD – JUNE 7th and 14th 1673

Afbeelding, en curieus Verhaal, van de derde
Zee slagh der *Nederlanderen*, victorieus bevochten,
tegen de t'zaam-gevoegde machtige Zee-Vlooten van
Vrankryk, en *Engelandt*. Op den 11 *Augusti*, des
Jaers 1673.

Aanwijzinge der cijfers, op het Esquadre van den Admirael Tromp, vechtende tegen het Blaauw Esquadre van den Engelschen
Admirael *Sir Edvert Sprag*.

Aanwijzinge der letteren, in de Esquadres van d'Heer
Luytenant Admirael Generael de Ruyter, en den Admirael Bankert,
vechtende tegens de Franse en Engelse Esquadrons.

vSt2531   FM2468   not signed, address M. Doornik,
Amsterdam 1673   28.6 × 49.6 cm

THE THIRD SEA-BATTLE OF THE
ENGLISH AND DUTCH FLEETS NEAR
KIJKDUIN – AUGUST 21st 1673

I : vSt-supp. FM2483 not signed, address J. de
    Ram, Amsterdam on text-leaf   29 × 40 cm
II: FM2801 This plate was adapted for the sea-
    battle near Bevesier June 30th 1690 (with
    portraits of Lord Herbert and Marq. of Previlly)

I : vSt2542 FM2495a H97 Romeyn de Hooge fecit, address Marcus Doornick Amsterdam. Poem by L(udwig) B(aronet) v(on) W(olzogen) ?   41 × 52.7 cm

II: see Siege and capture of Grave 1674 p. 86

SIEGE AND REDUCTION OF NAARDEN, HOL-
LAND – SEPTEMBER 12th 1673

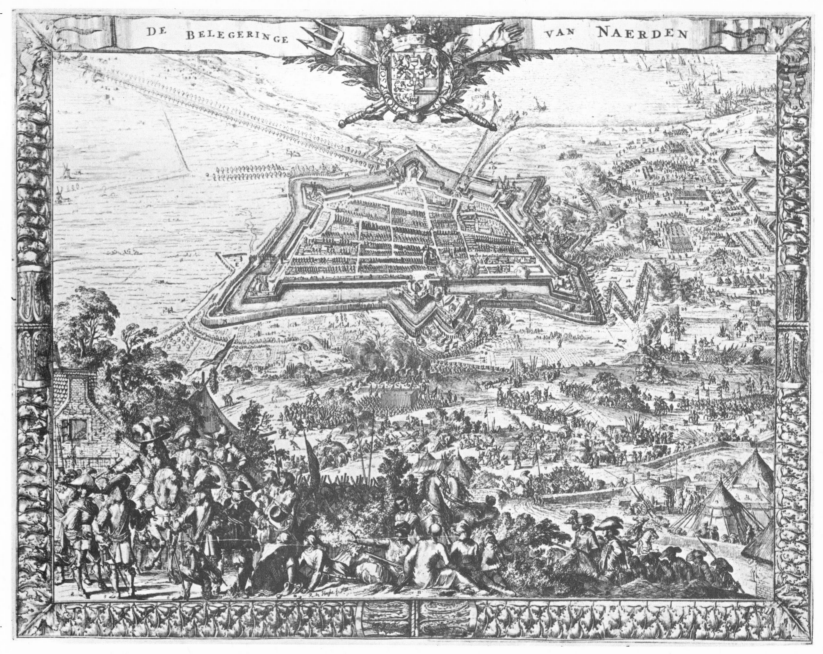

DE BELEGERINGE VAN NAERDEN

vSt2544 FM2500 R. de Hooghe f. 1673, address M.
Doornick, Amsterdam   32 × 42.6 cm

A DIKE BURSTING NEAR COEVORDEN, HOL-
LAND – OCTOBER 1st 1673

uyt gegeven t'Amsterdam by Marcus Doornick   R. de Hooge fecit.

I : FM2504b H98 before the letters and the verse
   36.5 × 47 cm
II: vSt2545 FM2504a R. de Hooge fecit, address M.
   Doornick, verse by H. Selijns

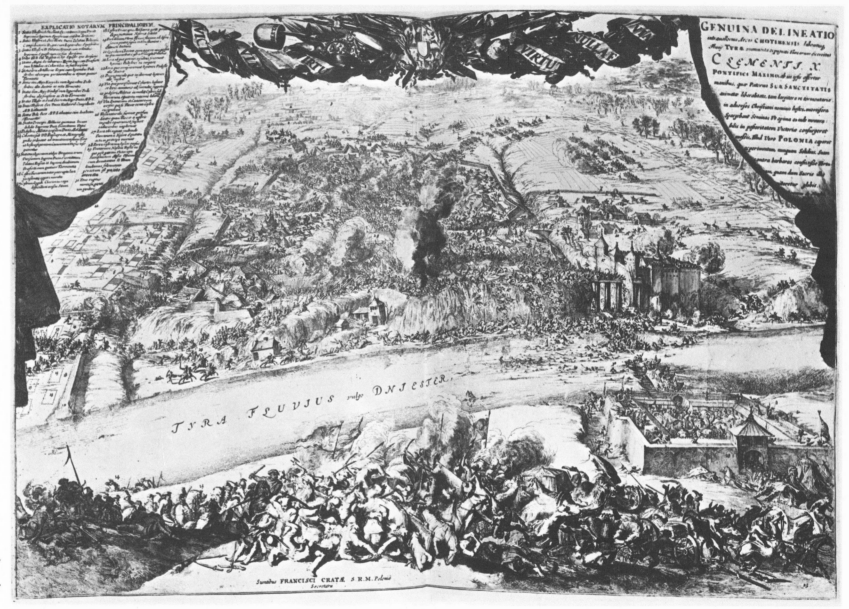

Albertina Vienna. H101 Romanus de Hooghe fecit,
sumptibus Fr. Gratae   45.5 × 67 cm
A small copy in Pierre van der Aa. *La Galerie
Agreable du Monde,* no date

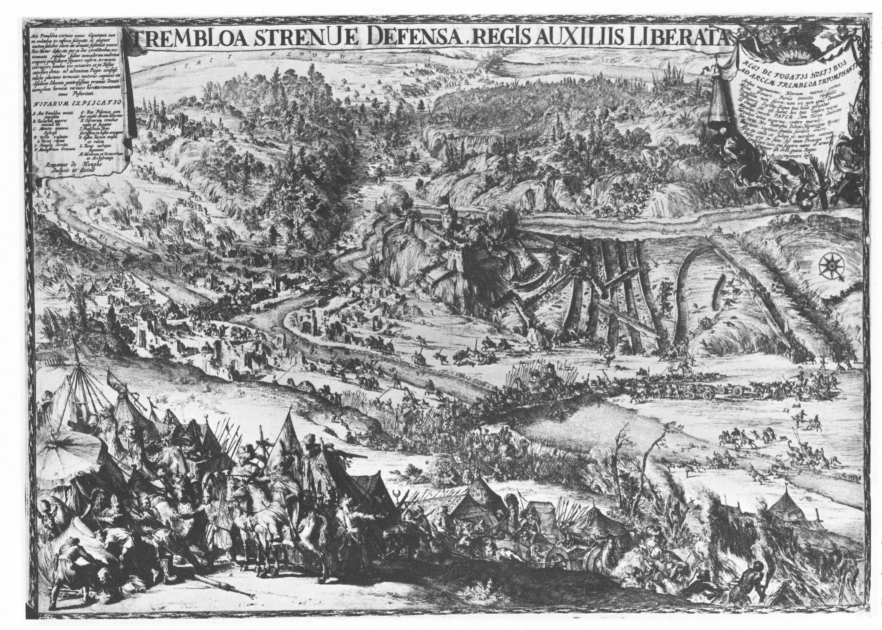

Prentenkabinet Leiden. H101 Romanus de
Hooghe Sculpsit et Cecinit, no address
48.2 × 71 cm
A small copy in Pierre van der Aa. *La Galerie
Agreable du Monde,* no date,   27 × 34 cm
Dessiné sur les lieux par Francois Grata,
gravé par Rom. de Hooge, text-lines altered on
top and added underneath

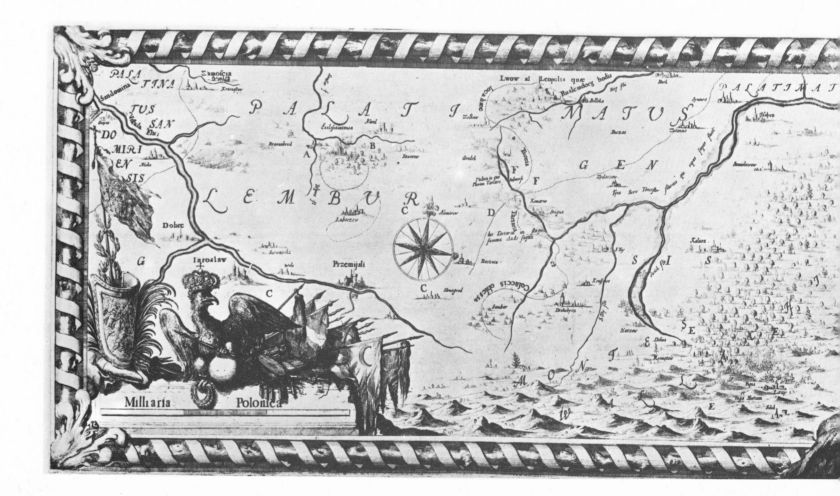

Albertina Vienna. DDD Romanus de Hooghe, no address
three leaves, each c.   25 × 47 cm

IOANNI
POLONORUM etc R
UBIQUE · TRIUMPHAN

D.D.D. ROMANUS DE HOOGHE

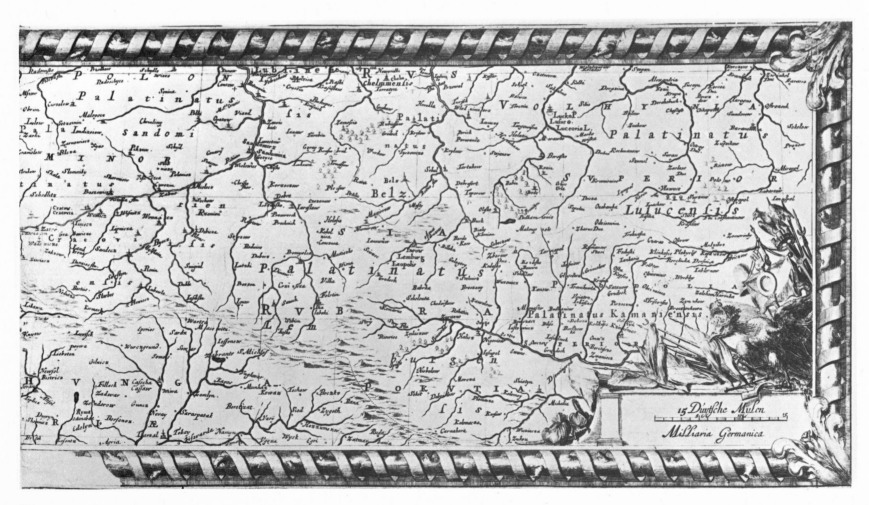

WILLEM III CAPTURING BONN, BREUIL
AND RYNBACH, GERMANY – NOVEMBER
2nd to 13th 1673

vSt2546 FM2506a + supp. H100 not signed,
address on text-leaf H. Sweerts, Amsterdam
26.2 × 38.2 cm

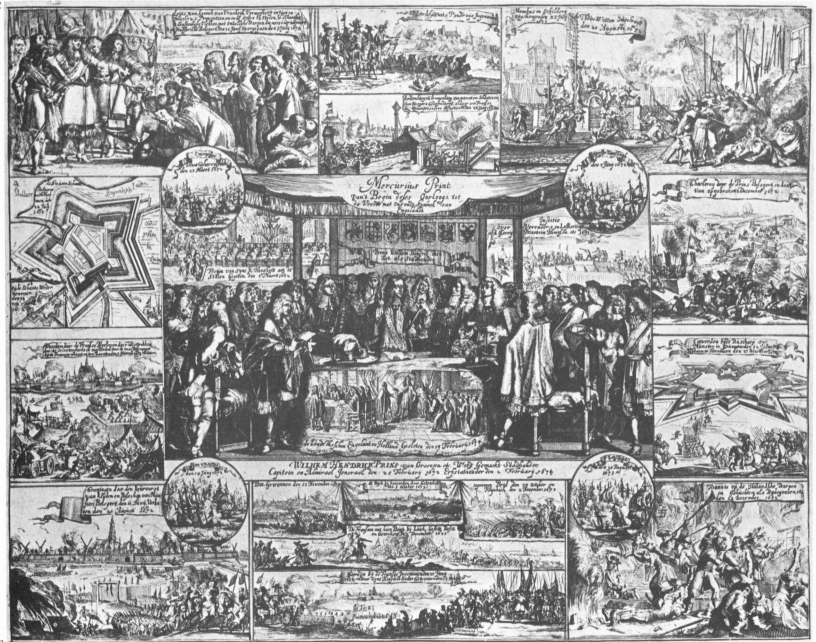

vSt2582 FM2530 not signed, no address   37.5 × 49.5 cm

vSt2584 FM2532 H111 Romyn de Hooghe fecit, invenit
et excudit... 1674   47.2 × 55.7 cm
The centre piece showing fire-works at The Hague is
often found separately

THE PROVINCE OF UTRECHT REJOINING THE
UNION OF PROVINCES – 1674

I   : vSt2593 FM2512a H99 before the letter
      40.5 × 51.2 cm
II : vSt2593 signed: Door Romeyn de Hooghe with his
      address, 1674
III: see The titular duchy of Gelre... 1675 p. 91

TRIOMPHE
de
JEAN III. SOBIESKI,
Roi de Pologne, Grand Duc de Lithuanie, Ukraine, etc. etc. etc.
qui lui fut decerné à Son Couronnement en l'an 1674 pour faire honneur aux
Victoires remportées par lui Sur les Turcs, Tartares, Cosaques,
etc.
Dessiné par François Grata, Secretaire de Sa Majesté, et gravé par Rom. de Hooge.
a Leide. Chez Pierre vander Aa avec Privilege.

I : Albertina Vienna. Romanus de Hooghe fecit 1675,
    with Latin dedication to John III, sumptibus Francisci
    Gratae   c. 47 × 68 cm
– : A small copy in Pierre van der Aa. *La Galerie Agreable
    du Monde*, no date dessiné par Fr. Grata, gravé par
    R. de Hooge   c. 27 × 35 cm
II: see Coronation of Joseph I 1690 p. 163

THE ALLIED TROOPS UNDER WILLEM
III AND THE FRENCH TROOPS UNDER
CONDÉ BATTLING NEAR SENEFFE,
BELGIUM – AUGUST 11th and 12th 1674

I : vSt2597 FM2549 H112 Romyn de Hooghe
    f. 1674, no address   30 × 43.3 cm
II : vSt2912 FM2890 + supp. adapted for the
    battle at Landen July 29th 1693, signature
    replaced by the address of Carel Allard,
    Amsterdam
III: vSt3156 FM3449 adapted for the battle of
    the allied troops near Bergen, with the
    address of A. Allard, Amsterdam

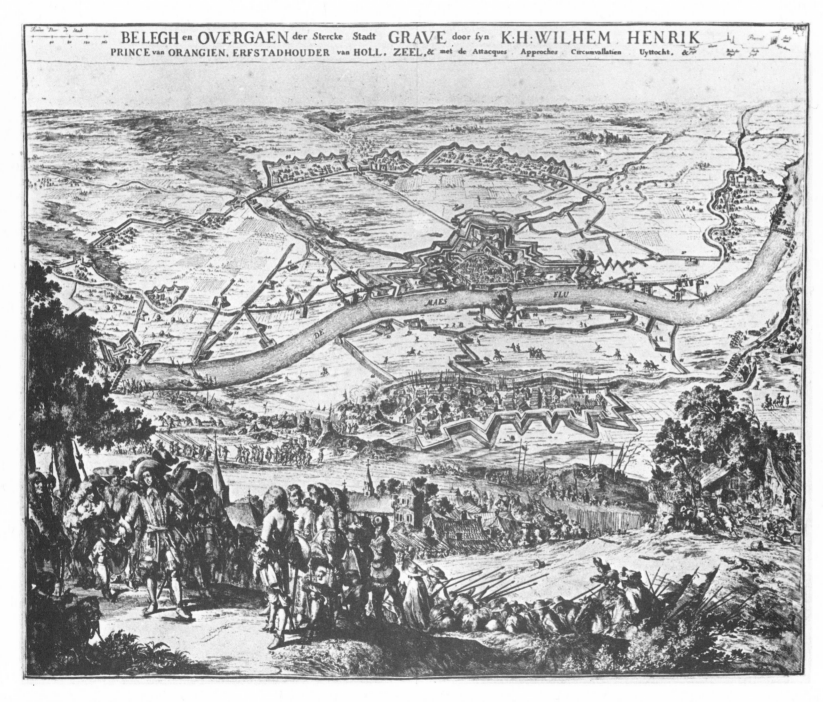

BELEGH en OVERGAEN der Stercke Stadt GRAVE door syn K:H: WILHEM HENRIK PRINCE van ORANGIEN. ERFSTADHOUDER van HOLL. ZEEL, & met de Attacques. Approches. Circumvallatien. Uyttocht. &

MAES
FLU
DE

WILLEM III BESIEGING AND CAPTURING
GRAVE – JULY 25th to 28th OCTOBER 1674

vSt2601 FM2559 not signed, no address   42.5 × 53.8 cm

De Stercke Stadt Grave, verovert door syn Koninckl. Hoogheyt de H. Prince van Oranje den 28 Octob. A:. 1674.

II: vSt2602 FM2561 H113 not signed, address
   Marcus Doornick, Amsterdam   41 × 52.7 cm
I : see Siege and reduction of Naarden 1673 p. 71

vSt2604 FM2565 not signed, address of De
Hooghe on text-leaf   24.2 × 35 cm

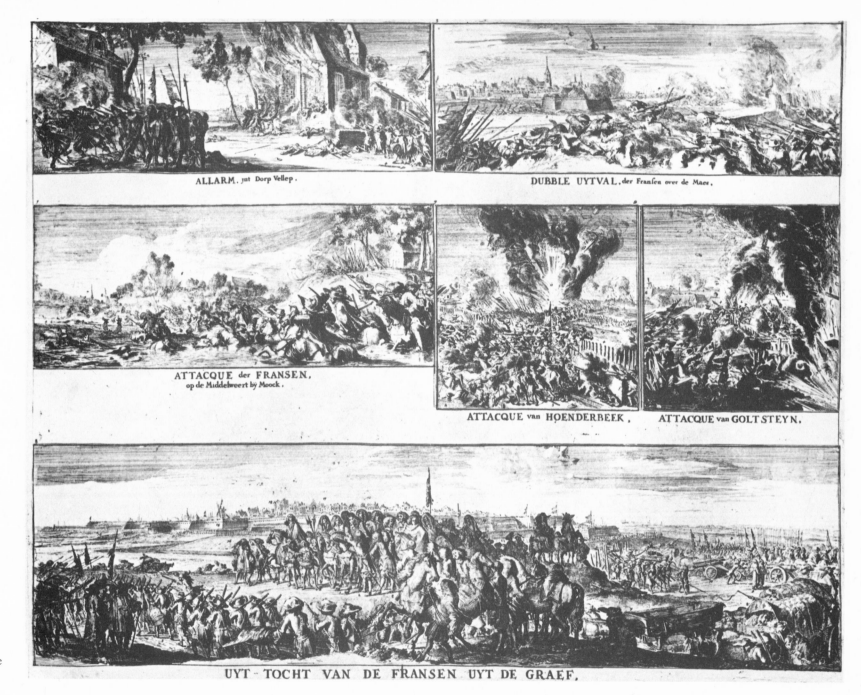

ALLARM, jnt Dorp Vellep.

DUBBLE UYTVAL, der Franfen over de Maes.

ATTACQUE der FRANSEN,
op de Middelweert by Moock.

ATTACQUE van HOENDERBEEK.

ATTACQUE van GOLT STEYN.

UYT - TOCHT VAN DE FRANSEN UYT DE GRAEF.

vSt2601 FM2559 not signed, address of De
Hooghe, Amsterdam   40.8 × 53.8 cm

I : FM2569a H114 not signed, no address, below blank
   space with caption: "Almanack voor 1675"
   68 × 46.6 cm
II : vSt2613 FM2569b not signed, address H. & D.
   Boom, below "Princelycke Almanach"
III: see *Kayserlicher Triumphkalender* 1676 p. 107

I : vSt2559 H102 not signed, address H. & D. Boom.
    68 × 47 cm
II : vSt2561 FM2515a R. de Hooghe f., the same address
III: FM2515b/c before the numbers and almanac
IV: without the almanac but with the caption "Prael-
    tooneel... 1674" alternatively "Neerlands Helden-
    Toneel"
— Another copy in Atlas van Stolk with the caption
    "Oraniens Ehrentempel"

III : vSt2616 FM2571 H115 Romyn de Hooghe, f. et in
Anno 1675   40 × 52 cm
Copperplate of earlier state retouched above and
additions below
I/II: see The province of Utrecht rejoining the Union of
Provinces 1674 p. 82

VICTORY OF FREDERICK WILLIAM ELECTOR
OF BRANDENBURG OVER THE SWEDES NEAR
FEHRBELIN – JUNE 26th to JULY 2nd 1675

vSt supp. H119 not signed, text-leaf with address of
De Hooghe, Amsterdam 1675   24.5 × 31.3 cm

Men kapt. men schiet. men herst. men slaet. Met ijsselyck Getier
Of menigh schoon het swaert ontgaet. moet dickmaels nogh door't Vier.

Vier
AUGUSTUS.
Pieter Nolpe Feett & Excud.

Le cœur le plus hardy lors que Bellone tonne, Fend l'air de mille esclairs, & quàm n'est sur les flots
Que l'effroyable cri des mourants matelots Que l'eau, le fer, le feu moissone, en fin s'espoune.

II: vSt2620 FM2574 + supp. Pieter Nolpe Fecit et Excud.
38 × 52.2 cm
Second state of a plate originally etched for the battle
of Lens, August 20th 1648, adapted for this battle by
De Hooghe with addition of two medallion portraits

SIEGE AND CONQUEST OF WISMAR BY
CHRISTIAN IV OF DENMARK – OCTOBER
17th to NOVEMBER 18th 1675

Leyden University L. H120 not signed, no address
49.5 × 64.5 cm

vSt2622 FM2577 H120a not signed, no address
27 × 34.3 cm

DEATH AND FUNERAL OF AMALIA VAN
SOLMS IN DELFT – DECEMBER 21st 1675

HET LYCK UYTGEDRAGEN   HET BEDT VAN PARADE.   HET LYCK TER AERDE BESTELT.

LYKSTATIE VAN HARE HOOGHEYT   DE PRINCESSE DOUARIERE.

vSt2623 FM2578 not signed, no address   c. 46 × 55 cm
see also LA127

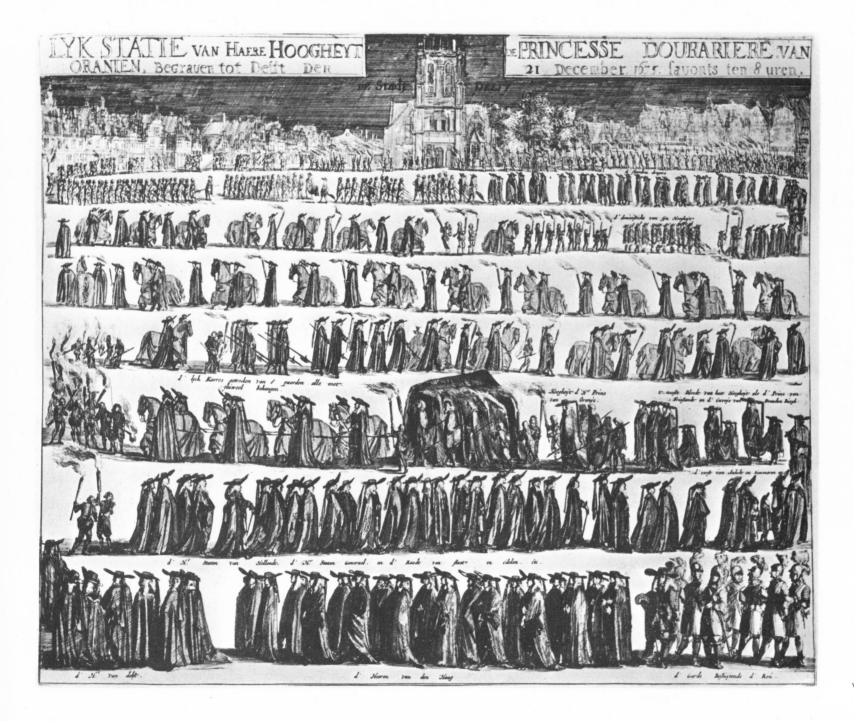

vSt2623 FM2578 not signed, no address   c. 43 × 53 cm

I : vSt2624 FM2304 H82 uytgegeven tot Amst. by
   Romeyn de Hooghe   45 × 55.5 cm
II : FM2304 supp. with the address of J. de Ram, Amster-
   dam
III: FM2304 with the address of N. Cornel & W. van
   Bergen, Rotterdam and Breda c. 1785

CAPTUM PHILIPSBURGUM Aº 1576

CHARLES V OF LORRAINE, HENRY
VON BADEN-DURLACH ETC. BESIEG-
ING PHILIPSBURG, GERMANY – MAY
to SEPTEMBER 17th 1676

vSt2633 FM2588 H122 Romanus de Hooghe
Amstlobatavus fec, no address   53 × 86.5 cm

THE ALLIED DANISH AND DUTCH SEAFORCES
UNDER CORNELIS TROMP CONQUERING THE
SWEDISH FLEET – JUNE 11th 1676

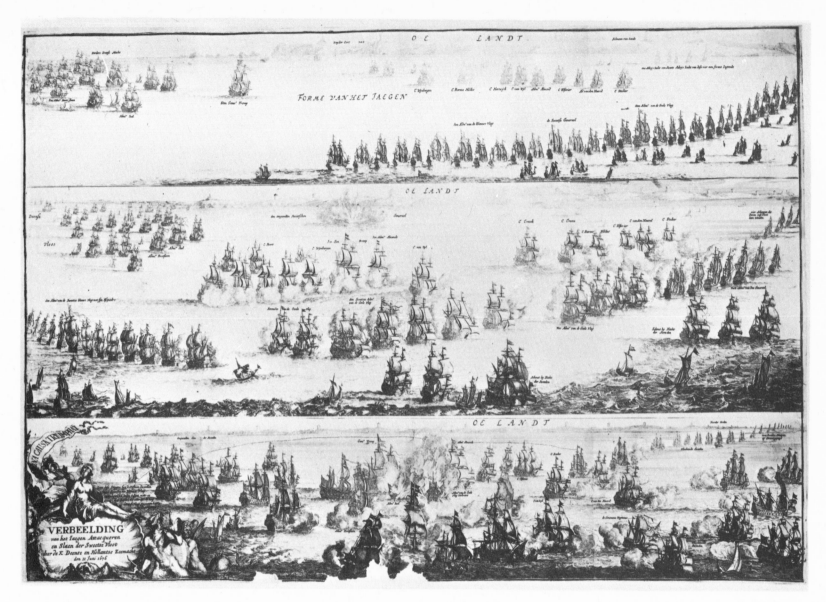

FM2590 not signed, no address   47 × 67 cm

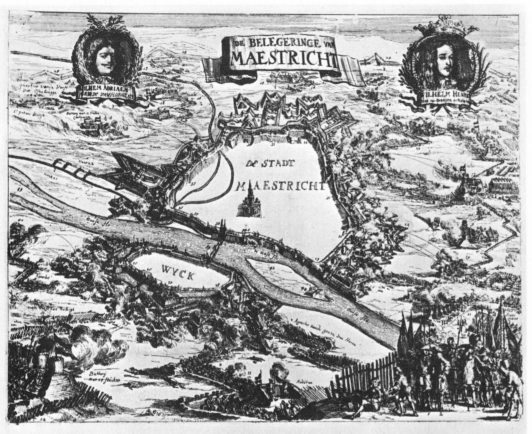

vSt supp. FM2592 not signed, address H. Sweerts,
Amsterdam   26.7 × 34.5 cm

vSt2635 FM2587 + supp. H121 Latin dedication by De
Hooghe   42.5 × 53.7 cm

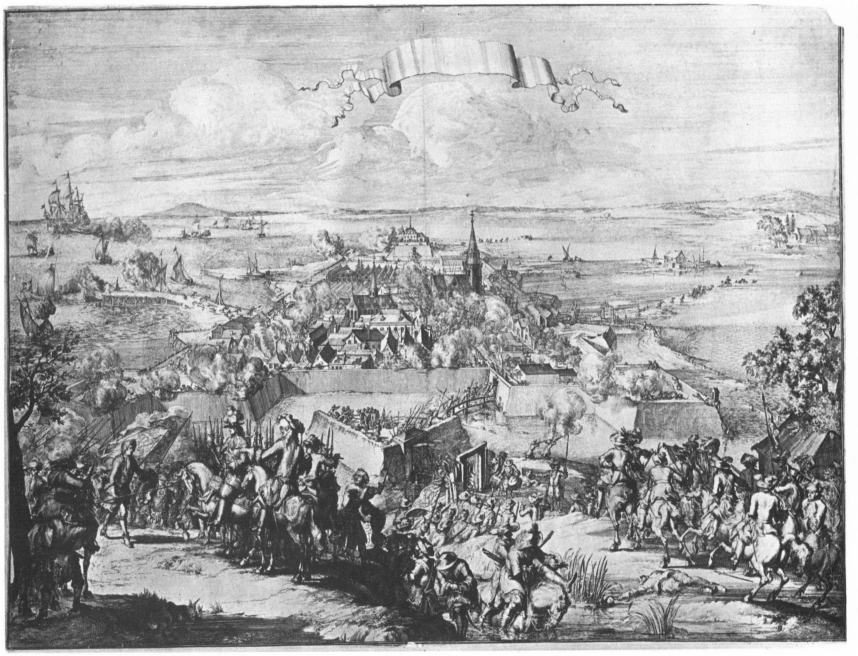

vSt supp. H123 not signed, no address
50 × 69.5 cm

I : vSt2625 FM2579 dedication by De Hooghe to
Amsterdam's Magistrates   47.5 × 57.2 cm

II : added on both sides of the dedication hatchings, below
the fifth column imperial globe, below the eighth
column two spear-points

III: added a twig of laurel to both sides of the imperial
globe

vSt2625 FM2579 not signed, no address   48 × 58 cm

vSt2626 FM2580 address Amst. H. & D. Boom
69 × 46.5 cm

III : Albertina Vienna. not signed, address Leonard
Christoph Locher 1676   68 × 46.6 cm
I/II: see Allegory on the victory in 1674 p. 89

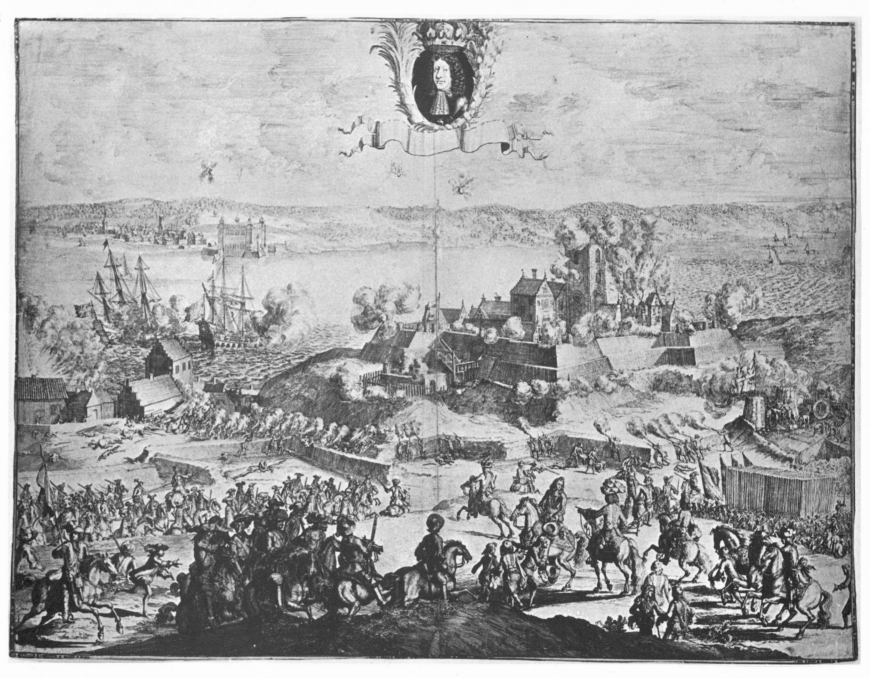

vSt supp. H128 not signed, no address
49 × 68 cm

ADMIRAL D'ESTREES AND COMMANDER
BINKES BATTLING NEAR THE ISLE OF
TOBAGO, WEST INDIES – FEBRUARY/MARCH
1677

vSt2648 FM2601 H125 text and dedication to the
Admiralty of Amsterdam by De Hooghe.
Reproduced from a coloured copy   41 × 50.5 cm

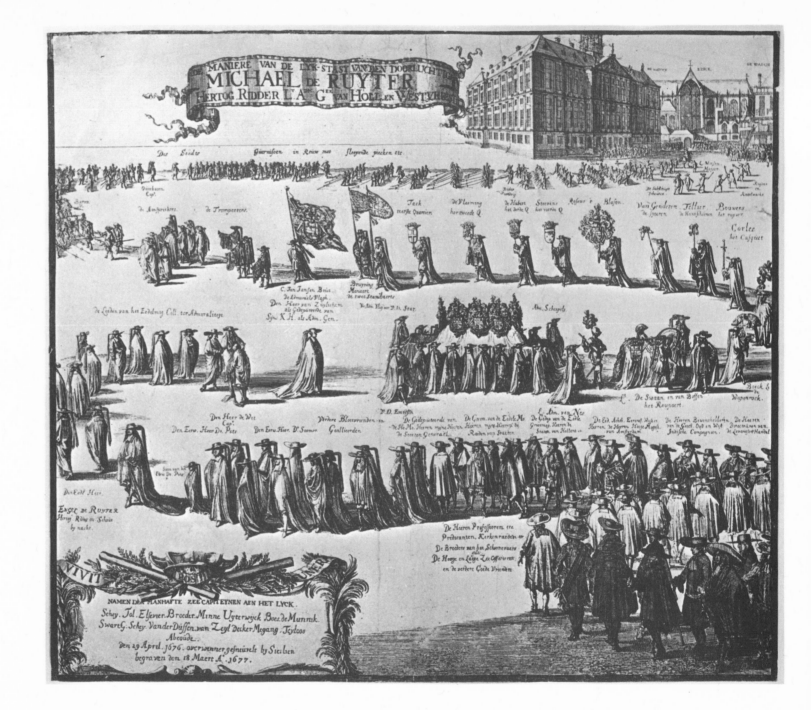

vSt2650 FM2602 not signed, no address   39.5 × 46.5 cm

VEROVERING van STETTIN

CAPTURE OF STETTIN BY FREDERICK
WILLIAM ELECTOR OF BRANDENBURG – 1677

Albertina Vienna. not signed, no address   42 × 52 cm

111

CAPTURE OF MARSTRAND AND
CARLSTEN BY GENERAL GYLDEN-
LOEVE – JULY 23rd 1677

Teyler Museum, Haarlem. H129 DDD
Romanus de Hooghe Amstlobatavus
46 × 69.5 cm

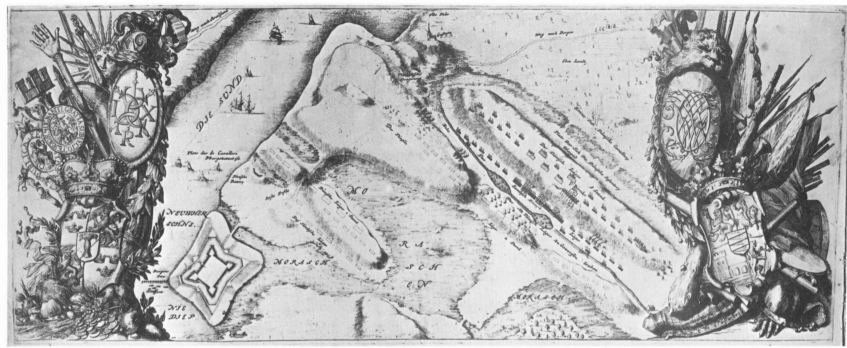

ALLEGORY ON THE MARRIAGE OF WILLEM III
TO MARY STUART AND THE WEDDING CERE-
MONY IN LONDON – NOVEMBER 14th 1677

vSt2661 FM2621 H127 R. de Hooghe sculpens canebut,
below: Romanus de Hooghe inv. et fecit   65.5 × 46.5 cm

I : vSt2642 FM2595b H124 Romeyn de Hooghe fecit et
   excudit 1677; with caption below as reproduced
   70 × 46.7 cm
II: blank space filled with text and caption "Princelijke
   Almanach... 1677"

CAMPAIGN OF CHRISTIAN IV OF DENMARK
ON THE ISLE OF RUGEN – 1678

I : Rijksmuseum Amsterdam. H130 not signed, no
   address   51 × 56 cm
II: see the Battle on the Boyne of Willem III, 1690

116

I : Teyler Museum, Haarlem. H130 not signed, no
address   54 × 67.5 cm
II: see the Battle on the Boyne of Willem III, 1690

117

COUNT STANISLAUS POTOCKI'S
MISFORTUNE NEAR MECHLIN,
BELGIUM – JULY 27th 1678

vSt2670 FM2619B supp. dedication to John III of
Poland by De Hooghe   47.5 × 70.2 cm

WILLEM III AND DUKE VILLA-HER-
MOSA BATTLING WITH THE COUNT
OF LUXEMBURG NEAR ST. DENIS,
HAINAUT – AUGUST 14th 1678

vSt2675 FM2629 H131 Romanus de
Hooghe Auctore Amsterdam, no address
54.8 × 83.5 cm

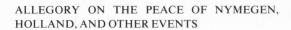

ALLEGORY ON THE PEACE OF NYMEGEN,
HOLLAND, AND OTHER EVENTS

vSt2676 FM2636 H132 By Romijn de Hooghe
65 × 46.3 cm

120

I : vSt2679 FM2638 Romeyn de Hooge, in de Wackeren
   Hont (Amst.)   47 × 54.5 cm
II : vSt2981 FM2976 adapted for the Peace of Ryswyk
   November 6th 1697, with addition of numbers, new
   date below the column and a poem by S. Donnet

I : vSt2688 FM2644 H133 R. de Hooge fecit, no address,
   with "almanak"   65.5 × 48 cm
II: vSt2688 FM2644 instead of the almanac, dedication to
   Amsterdam's Magistrates and their arms

122

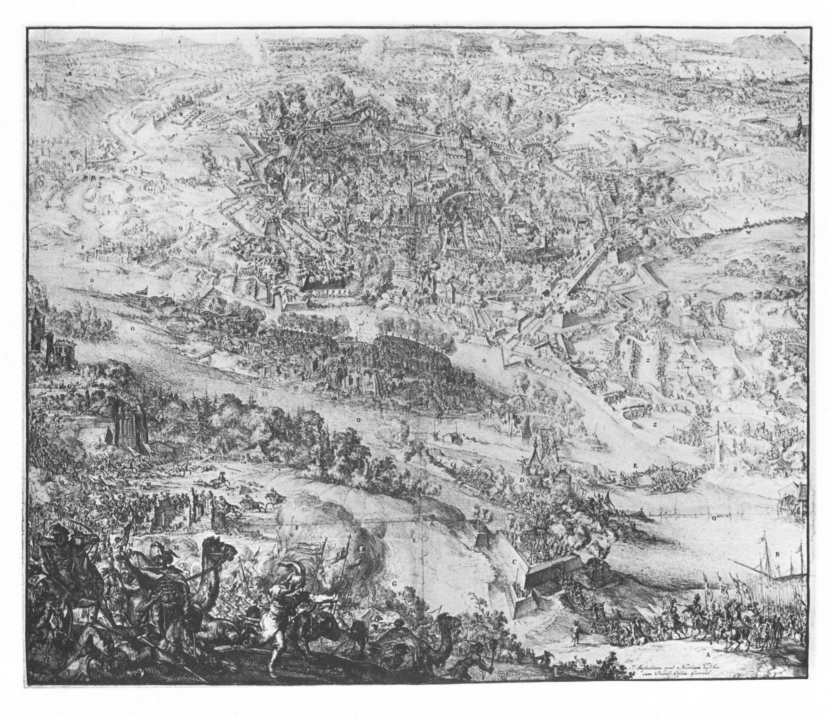

KARA MUSTAPHA BESIEGING VIENNA –
JULY 14th to SEPTEMBER 12th 1683

vSt2697 RDH, address Amstelodami apud Nicolaum
Visscher with text in French   45.2 × 56.5 cm

LUXEMBURG BOMBARDED BY MARSHAL DE
CREQUI – JUNE 4th 1684

vSt supp. FM2667 H134 ex conatibus Romani de Hooghe
et formis Nicolai Visscher   47.5 × 57 cm

124

125

Teyler Museum, Haarlem. Romanus de Hooghe S.R. Inv.
et Auct., no address, four leaves each c. 47 × 66 cm

PERSECUTION OF THE PROTESTANTS IN
FRANCE – 1685

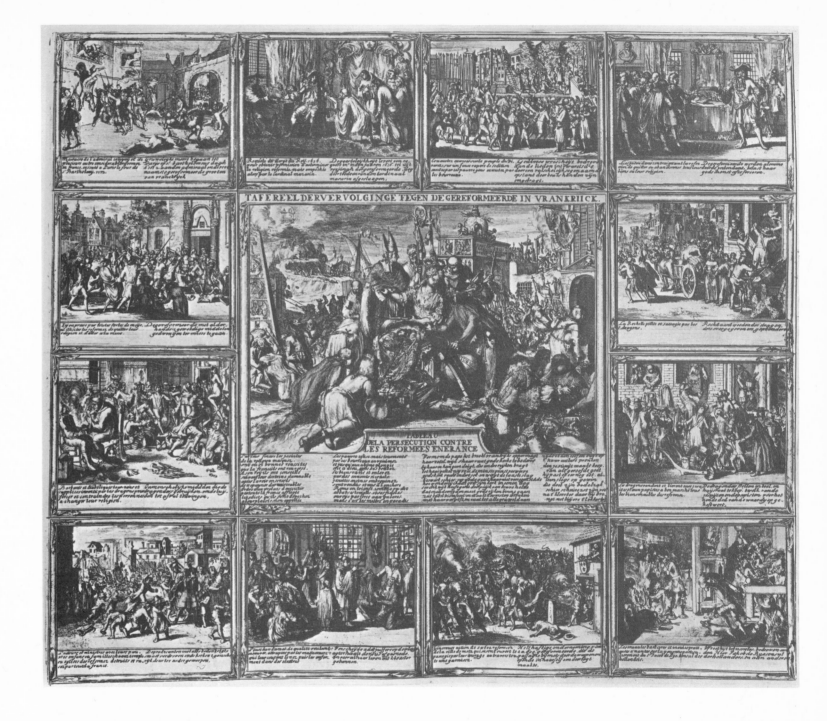

Albertina Vienna. FM2674 not signed, no address
42.6 × 52 cm

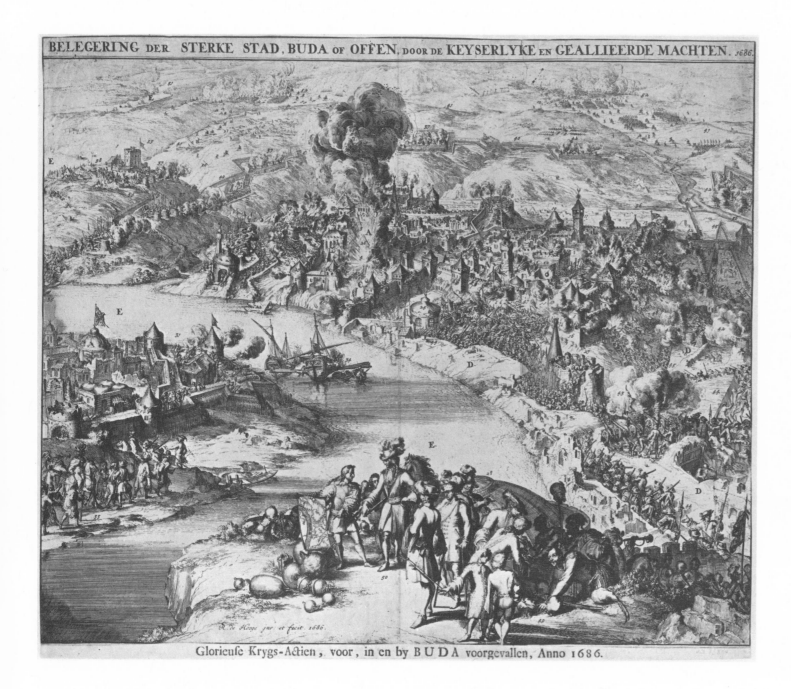

BELEGERING DER STERKE STAD, BUDA of OFFEN, DOOR DE KEYSERLYKE EN GEALLIEERDE MACHTEN. 1686.

R. de Hooge jnv. et fecit. 1686.

Glorieuse Krygs-Actien, voor, in en by BUDA voorgevallen, Anno 1686.

CHARLES V OF LORRAINE BESIEGING AND TAKING BY STORM BUDA – JUNE 21st (SEPTEMBER 2nd) 1686

I : "Belegering..." (siege) R. de Hooge jnv. et fecit, 1686
   46.5 × 56 cm
   Text-leaf in Dutch, French and German, with or without the address of A. D. Ooszaen
II: "Verovering..." (capture)

I : Museum Boymans-Van Beuningen. H57 R. de Hooge
fecit, no address   28.6 × 37 cm
II: According to Georg Rózsa (*Oud Holland* 1962 page
111) also with address of Thomas Wiering, Hamburg

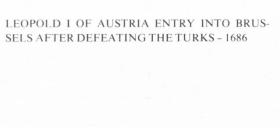

LEOPOLD I OF AUSTRIA ENTRY INTO BRUSSELS AFTER DEFEATING THE TURKS – 1686

DIVO et INVICTISSIMO
LEOPOLDO I.
P. F. A.
Fidei in Hungaria Assertori,
Rebellium Domitori,
Turcarum Debellatori,
Ob BUDAM septimò Inexpugnabilem
Armis Victricibus occupatam
Triumphales Brucellæ extinctæ
Dedicant Consecrantq;
AMR et GLORIA

VIENNA

NEUHEUSEL

PEST

ZEGEDIN

GRAN

Series of nine prints, unsigned without address, H263-H271.   c.35.5/38.7 × 54/57.5 cm
The prints are numbered 1 to 9; of the prints no. 1, 2, 5 and 8 two states are known namely before the letters, number and text, and with these

131

2. *Excellentissimo Belgii Gubernatore D. MARCHIONE DE GASTANAGA ex Aulâ per Cœmeterium Ædis Sacrae, cui à Sabulo nomen, progressuro exploduntur œnea Tormenta loci ibidem disposita, quibus ipso momento ex omnibus Regiae Urbis propugnaculis Machinae murales sonoro fragore circumquaque responsant.*

At enim CÆSARIS Nomen latiùs vulgatur Trophæis Bellicis, quàm Tormentis; horum sonus in unam Urbem exiit, illorum Fama in Uniuerſum Orbem.

3. *Excellentissimus D. Princeps De La Tour et Tassis è Palatio suo obviàm Excellentissimo Domino MARCHIONI DE GASTANAGA Belgii Gubernatori procedit, advenientem congressu officioso salutaturus.*

Principes convenerunt in unum, collaturi Consilium et Industriam ad celebrandos Augustissimi Cæsaris LEOPOLDI Triumphos, qui quidquid Æternæ Celebritatis Triumphis dignum gerit CONSILIO gerit et INDUSTRIA.

133

4. *Excellentiss: D. MARCHIO DE GASTANAGA cum Procerum Aulicorumque Comitatu deducitur in Palatium, ubi intùs forisque ad agendam cum Triumphali Pompâ Festæ Lucis Solennitatem adornari jusserat Omnia Excellentiss. D. Principis De La Tour &c. Munificentia.*

Quis, Quid ibi in Personis, seu in Rebus principem Magnificentiæ Titulum non promeruit? Excellebant simul Omnes et Omnia.

5. Exquisitus Tridinii apparatus, et Genialium Epularum splendidissimus Luxus, principis Celebritatis, quæ Convivio agebatur, Principum Personarum, quæ convivæ discumbebant, aut Convivis ministrabant, Principis, qui Convivas excipiebat, Excellentiâ dignus.

Nec Visu satiabatur oculus, nec auris Auditu. Sed quid de Gustu? Hunc satiârunt OMNIA et NIHIL. OMNIA, quia NIHIL uspiam deerat ad Deliciarum copiam; NIHIL, quia ubique aderant OMNIA ad copiæ Delicias.

135

IGNIUM NOCTURNA HILARIA

Noctem verterunt in Diem: idem in Hungariâ illustriùs suis Ignibus fecerunt Victricia CÆSARIS arma, ubi Noctem, cui prǽerat Turcica LUNA verterunt in Diem, cui prǽest
SOL IUSTITIÆ CHRISTUS.
Ideò AUSTRIACÆ GLORIÆ, cui Bruxellis in SABULO luxerunt, arseruntque Triumphales Ignes, non oblitetabitur in Sabulo, non disparebit cum Luce, non extinguetur cum Igne, verùm ad exteros posterosque propagabitur omni Ære perennius Monumentum.

136

7. *Excellentissimi D. Principis de La Tour Domesticus Hortus publicæ Lætitiæ Die ad publicam Voluptatem apertus.*

Nullus ad hunc Paradisum excubabat Cherubinus, qui accedentes repelleret armatus; Angelus è Principatibus urbanior unus liberè ingrediendi copiam faciebat.

137

8. *Aulæ Regiæ Bruxellensis (quæ Excellentiss. D. MARCHIONIS DE GASTANAGA Belgium pro Rege Gubernantis in præsentiâ Sedes) Area interior, ubi miri rarique Artificii Fons novus saliebat, et Artificiosis expugnandum Ignibus Castrum Triumphi assurgebat.*

Propria CÆSAREI cùm Honoris tùm Nominis Symbola, nec limpidiùs inspici possunt, quàm in Fonte, nec splendidiùs exhiberi, quàm in Igne.
CÆSARIS CONSILIUM et INDUSTRIA sunt Fons novus, à quo Victoriæ ceu riui jugiter manantes in DOMUM AUSTRIACAM fluunt.

Castrum Triumphi Lucens et Ardens.

Austriaci Cæsaris Insignia ad Triumphale hoc Castrum appensa conspiciuntur; cur non et adscripta leguntur LEOPOLDI IGNATII Augusta Nomina? Intelliguntur illa clariùs in Luce expressa et in Igne; quippe à Luce et Igne initiales si mutuéris Literas L I LEOPOLDVM IGNATIVM compendiò exscripsisti, unáque Orbi descripsisti LVCIDVM IGNEVM; LVCIDVM immortalibus Triumphis, IGNEVM fulminatricibus Armis.

VICTORY OF CHARLES V OF LORRAINE AND
MARGRAVE LOUIS OF BADEN-BADEN OVER
THE TURKS NEAR NAGYHARSANY, HUNGARY
– AUGUST 12th 1687

Rijksmuseum Amsterdam. H139 not signed, no address,
four leaves each   c.50 × 71 cm

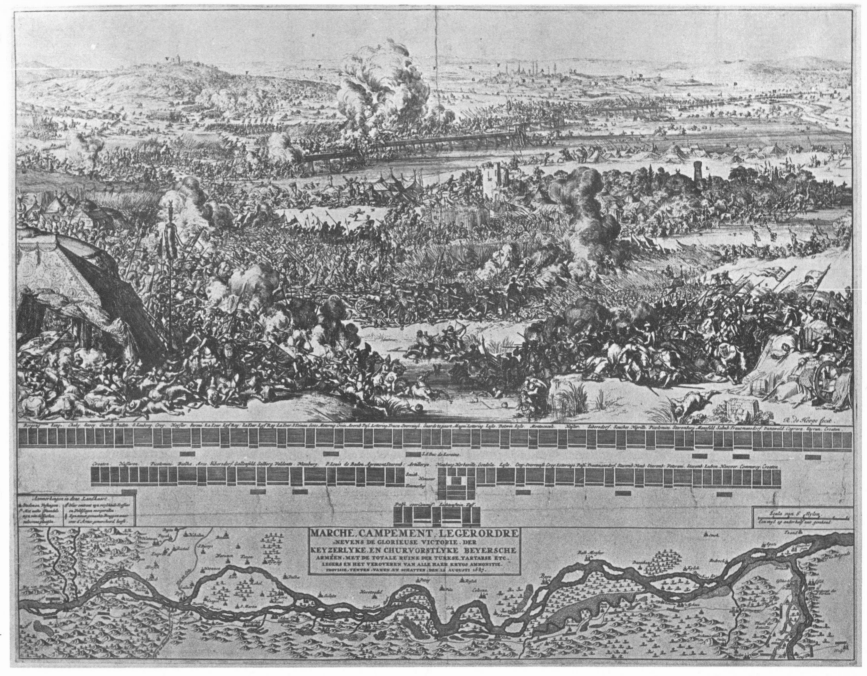

I : H140 R. de Hooge fecit, address on text-
   leaf Aert Dirksz Ooszaen   44 × 59.3 cm
II: see Victory at Slankamen 1691 p. 167

I : Albertina Vienna. Before the letter at the bottom
   67.5 × 45.3 cm
II: vSt2821 Romyn de Hooghe fecit, Ph. Bouttats Jr...
   and three text-lines below

POLITICAL EVENTS OF THE YEAR 1687

Koning - Spel Courant op 't Jaer 1687.

I : vSt2720 FM2685 before the signature, address
    J. Tangena   39 × 29.5 cm
II: vSt2720 signed Romain de Hooge fec

144

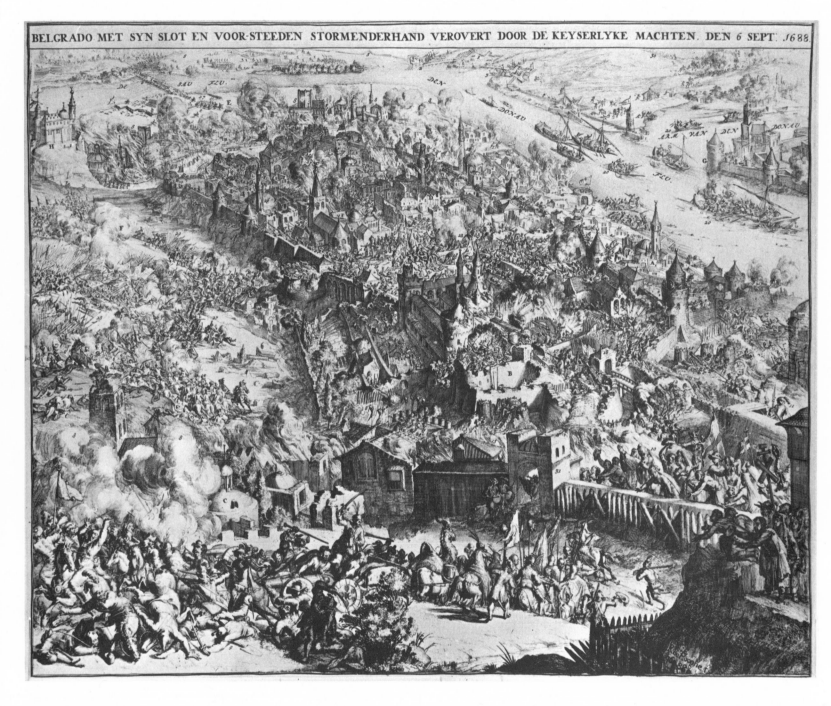

BELGRADO MET SYN SLOT EN VOOR-STEEDEN STORMENDERHAND VEROVERT DOOR DE KEYSERLYKE MACHTEN. DEN 6 SEPT. 1688.

BELGRAD TAKEN BY STORM BY MAXIMILIAN EMANUEL ELECTOR OF BAVARIA – SEPTEMBER 6th 1688

I : H146 R. de Hooghe f. 1686, no address
46 × 56.7 cm
II : vSt supp. R. de Hooghe f. 1688, no address
Lit.: Georg Rósza. *Romeyn de Hooghe und die Türkenkriege in Ungarn.* (*Oud Holland* 1962 pp. 101 ff.)

WILLEM III SETTING SAIL FOR ENGLAND
FROM THE MARINE BASE HELLEVOETSLUIS –
13th (*sic*) NOVEMBER 1688

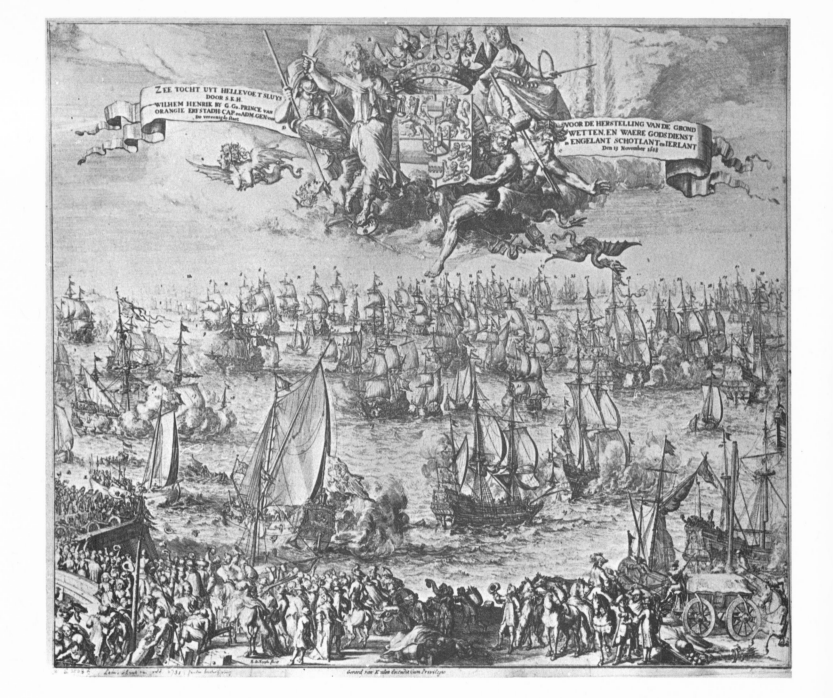

I : vSt2731 FM2708a H141 R. de Hooghe fecit, address
    J. Tangena, Leiden   47.5 × 57 cm
II : FM2708b with the numbers 1-61 instead of 1-12
III: vSt2732 the same signature, address Gerard van
    Keulen (Amst.)

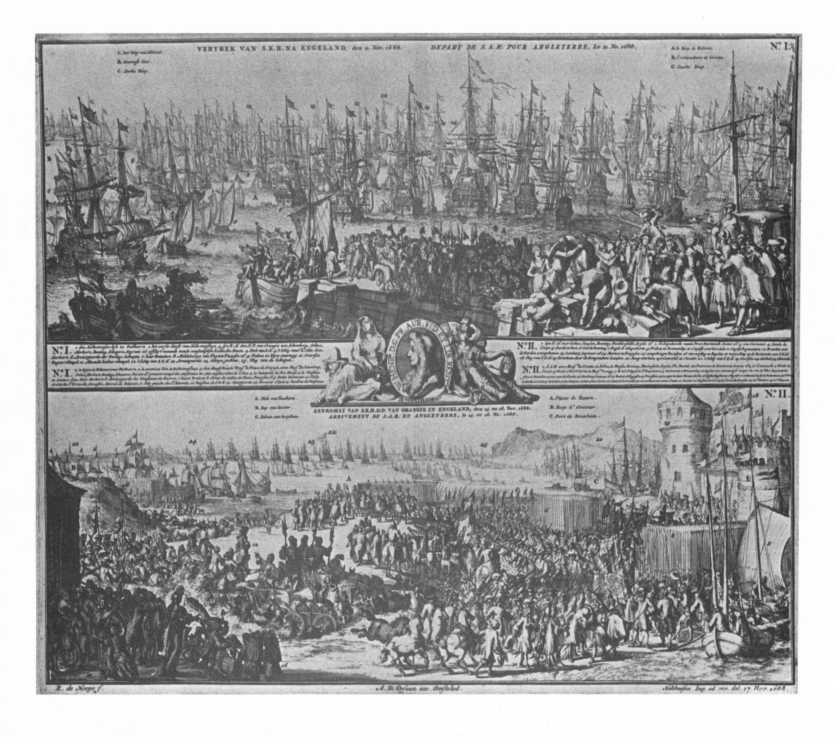

WILLEM III SETTING SAIL – NOVEMBER 11th
AND HIS ARRIVAL IN BRIXHAM (TORBAY) –
NOVEMBER 15th/16th 1688

I : vSt2742 FM2713a H142 R. de Hooge f. Hekhuisen…
   17 nov. 1688, address A. D. Oosaan, Amsterdam
   43.6 × 53.6 cm
II : vSt2742 FM2713b without Hekhuisen's name, address
   J. Covens en Mortier, in: De Larrey. *Geschiedenis van
   Engelandt…* 1728-1730. Vol. IV (1730)

147

WILLEM III SETTING SAIL – NOVEMBER 11th
AND HIS ARRIVAL IN BRIXHAM (TORBAY) –
NOVEMBER 15th/16th 1688

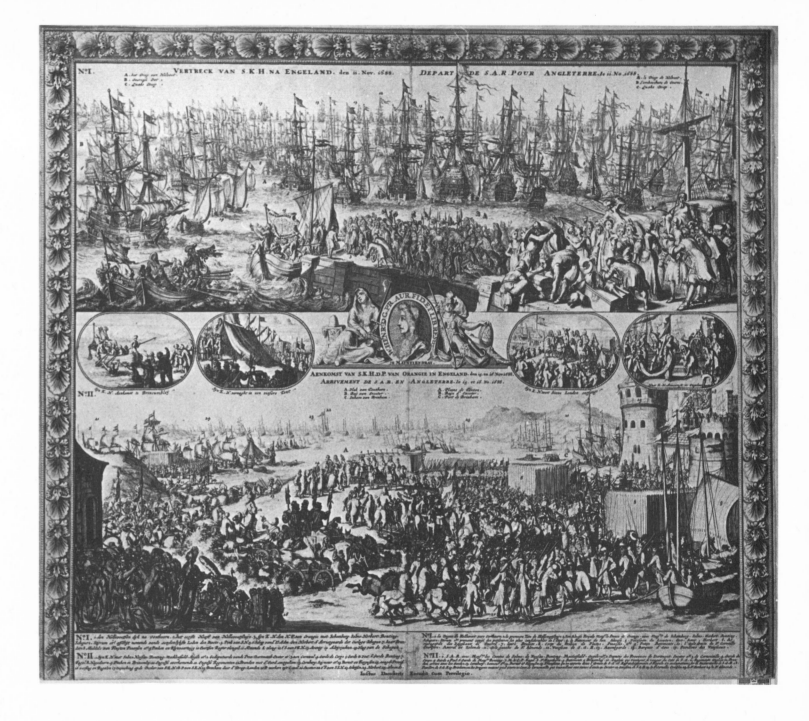

vSt supp. FM2714 not signed, address Justus Danckerts,
Amsterdam   50 × 59.2 cm

I : vSt2753 FM2720a H143 R. de Hooge fecit, address
      A. D. Oosaen   42.5 × 52.7 cm
II : FM2720b with the address on the tex-leaf in italics
III: FM2720 supp. with the address G. van Keulen,
      Amsterdam

ARRIVAL OF WILLEM III IN ENGLAND WITH
THE DUTCH FLEET – 1688

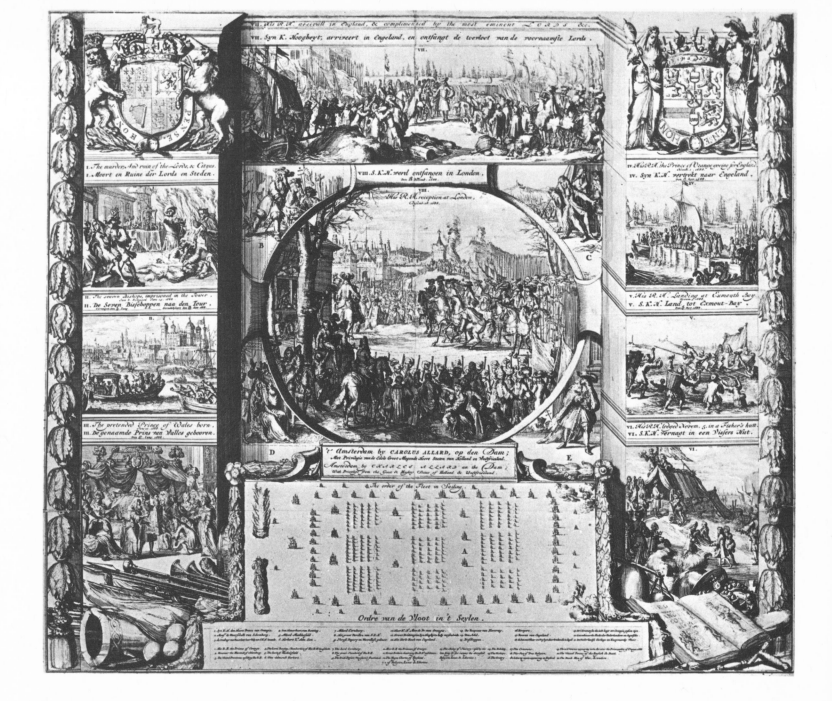

I : vSt2755 FM2722c H144 not signed, address Charles
   Allard, Amsterdam   49 × 58 cm
   with separate text-leaf by L. Smids and the same
   address
II: FM2722b with a cancel pasted over the central bottom
   part presenting the almanac for 1689

ALLEGORY ON THE ARRIVAL ÓF WILLEM III
WITH DUTCH FLEET IN ENGLAND – 1688

vSt2756 FM2722a R. de Hooge inv. et fec., address
Amst. Carolus Allard   97.8 × 58 cm

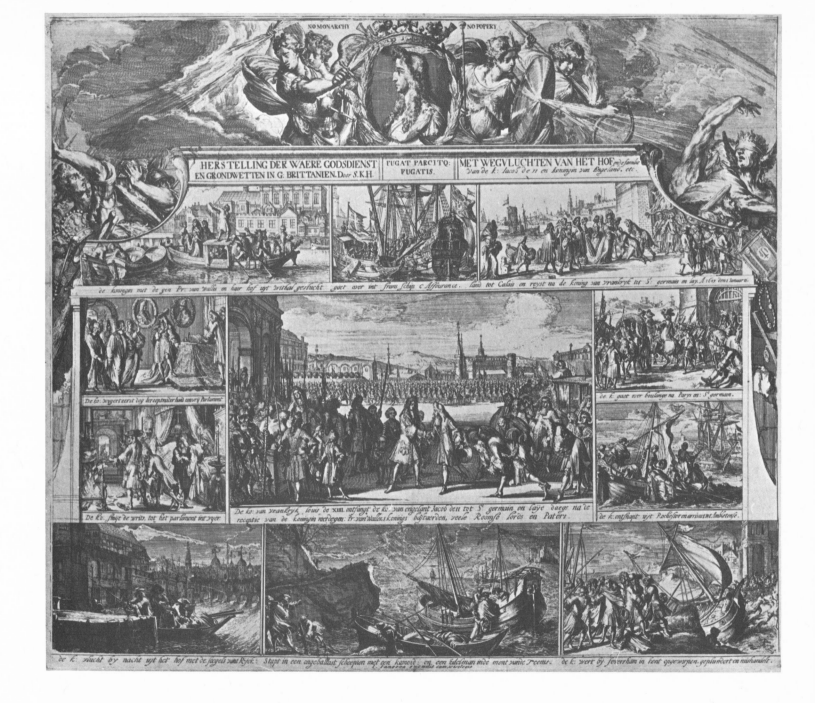

I : vSt2761 FM2751 not signed, address J. Tangena
    (Leiden)   47 × 56.2 cm
II: vSt2761 R. de Hooghe, the same address
The centre-part is often found separately (H79)

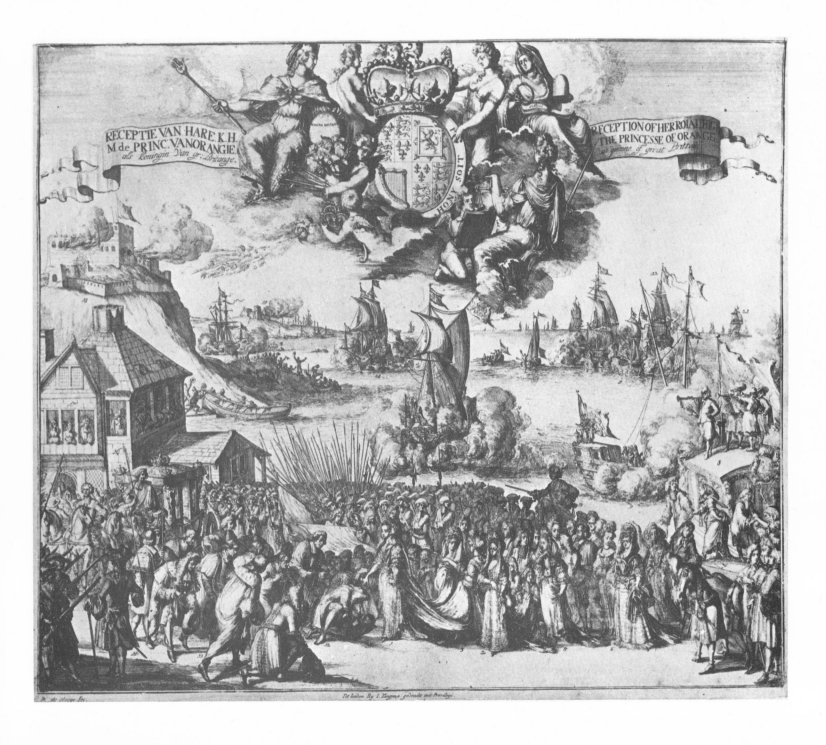

Albertina Vienna, vSt2773 FM2729 H147 R. de Hooge
fec., address Leiden I. Tangena   46 × 56 cm
with text in Dutch, French and English

CORONATION OF WILLEM III AND MARY
STUART IN WESTMINSTER ABBEY – APRIL 21st
1689

KROONING VAN WILLEM DE III. EN MARIA, TOT KONING EN KONINGIN VAN ENGELAND, ENZ. IN WESTMUNSTERS ABDY DEN 11/21 APRIL 1689.

Rang der hooge en laage Staats perzoonen, geleidende haare Majesteiten naar de Abdy, om gekroond te worden.

vSt2782 FM2733 H149 R. de Hooge fec., address
Carolus Allard   49 × 58 cm

154

I : vSt2784 H151 Romain de Hooge fec., no address
    51.5 × 60.5 cm
II: FM2735 the same signature, address I. Tangena

CORONATION OF WILLEM III AND MARY
STUART IN WESTMINSTER ABBEY – APRIL 21st
1689

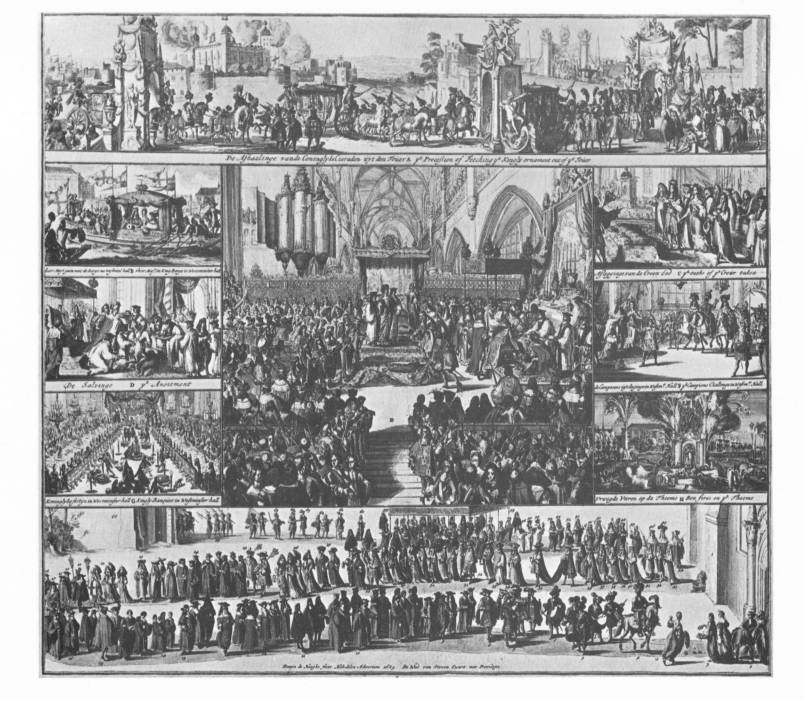

I : vSt2785 FM2734a H150 Romyn de Hooghe fecit
Hek(huyzen) del: Advivium, address Wed. van Steven
Swart, text in English and French 49.5 × 57.5 cm
II: FM2734b with caption „Alle de bijsond. en particul.
ceremon. – All the part. ceremonies"

FIREWORKS IN LONDON, LEIDEN, MAASTRICHT, AMSTERDAM, HE HAGUE, HAMBURG, BOIS-le-DUC, HAARLEM – APRIL 21st 1689

vSt2787 FM2743 R. de Hooghe fecit, address P. Rotterdam, Amst.   50.5 × 58.5 cm
Reproduced from a coloured copy

N.9. Vuir-staken en Vreugt-bewysen, door de Ed:Agtb: Heeren van de Regering tot Haarlem, op de Markt, Toorens etc. den 21. April 1689.

I : vSt2789 FM2738a H153 R. de Hooge fecit, address
Amst., P. Rotterdam with text-leaf in Dutch and
French   47.5 × 57 cm

II : vSt supp. FM2738b Queen Anna on the throne (1702)
R. de Hooge, the same address

III: vSt2790 FM2738c King George II on the throne,
address J. Covens en Mortier (1728) in: De Larrey.
Geschiedenis van Engelandt... Amst. 1728-1730.
Vol. I p. 766

LONDONDERRY, IRELAND; THE SIEGE OF
BONN, GERMANY – APRIL 29th ; JUNE 29th 1689

LONDONDERRI

BELEGERING VAN BON

I : vSt2808 FM2786 supp. not signed, address Leiden,
J. Tangena   46.5 × 55.5 cm
Often these parts are found separately
II: FM2847 the upper part was used for the Siege of
Athlone, 1691

160

BATTLE BETWEEN THE PRINCE OF
WALDECK AND MARSHAL DE HUMIE-
RES NEAR WALCOURT, BELGIUM –
AUGUST 25th 1689

I : vSt2811 FM2788 not signed, address in the
    text J. Robyn Amst. 1689   13.6 × 46 cm
II: adapted for the battle at Neerwinden, July
    29th 1693

I : FM2780 before the letter and with the
almanac   56.5 × 95 cm
II: vSt2812 FM2780 H162 Mr. Romain de
Hooge fecit, address J. Tangena

CORONATION OF JOSEPH I KING OF
HUNGARY, AUGSBURG – FEBRUARY 14th
1690

II: Albertina Vienna. not signed, address A. Schoo-
    nebeek, Amst.   c.47 × 68 cm
I : see Coronation of John III of Poland 1674 p. 83

VICTORY OF WILLEM III OVER THE
UNITED IRISH AND FRENCH
TROOPS ON THE BOYNE – JULY 12th
1690

II: Prentenkabinet Leiden. FM2804a H165
    Latin dedication to Willem III and Mary
    Stuart by De Hooghe, the numbers
    removed   54 × 116.5 cm
I : see Campaign of Christian IV of Den-
    mark 1678 p. 116, 117

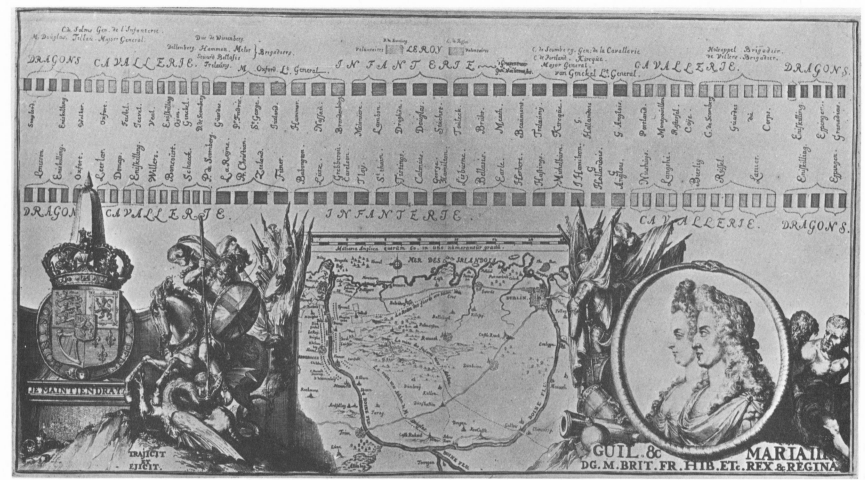

VICTORY OF WILLEM III OVER THE UNITED IRISH AND FRENCH TROOPS ON THE BOYNE – JULY 12th 1690

Prentenkabinet Leiden. FM2804a H165 not signed, address on text-leaf B. Beeck, The Hague; this plate supplements the preceding one   25.5 × 50 cm

JAMES II OF ENGLAND FLEEING-VICTORY OF
WILLEM III OVER THE UNITED IRISH AND
FRENCH TROOPS NEAR DROGHEDA – JULY 12th
1690

I : vSt2844 FM2805 H166 dedication by De Hooghe,
    address C. Allard   49 × 58.5 cm
II: FM3465 The lower part adapted for the battle near
    Zaragoza August 20th 1710

Gelukkige en seer groote Victorie, door Syne Doorluchtigheyd den Heer Markgraaf Lodewyk van Baden tegens de Turksche Armée
bevochten, tusschen Peter Waradyn ende Salankement, den 19. Augusti 1691.

II: Albertina Vienna, R. de Hooge fecit, address
    J. de Ram on text-leaf   c.28 × 60 cm
I : compare Victory of Charles V of Lorraine
    1686 p. 142 Lit.: Georg Rósza. *Romeyn de
    Hooghe und die Türkenkriege in Ungarn*, in
    Oud Holland 1962 pp. 101 ff.

SEA-BATTLE BETWEEN THE ALLIED
AND ENGLISH AND FRENCH FLEETS
NEAR CAPE LA HOGUE, FRANCE –
MAY 29th 1692

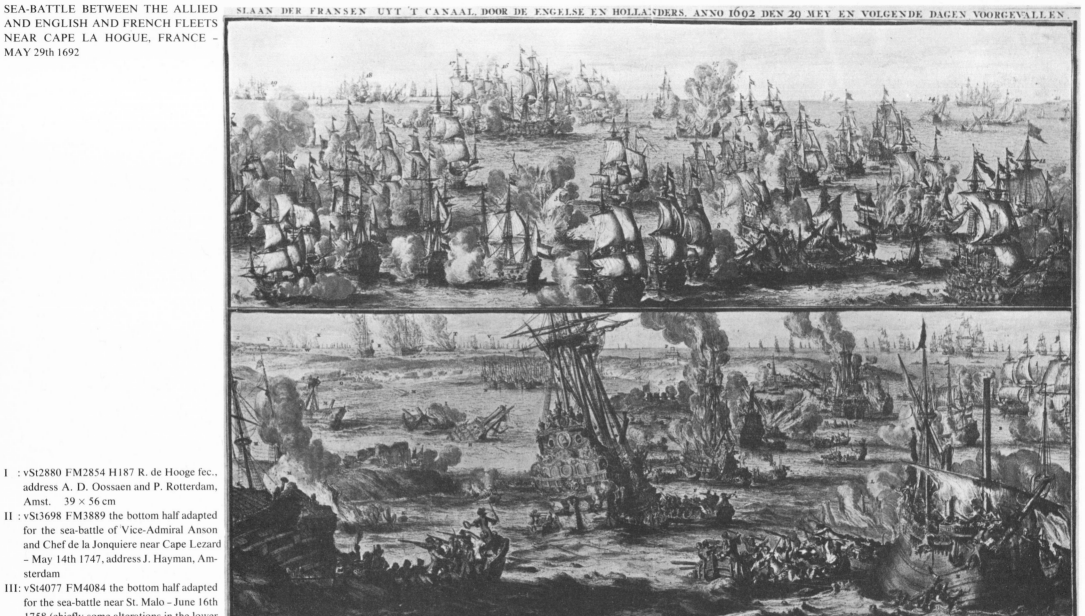

SLAAN DER FRANSEN UYT 'T CANAAL, DOOR DE ENGELSE EN HOLLANDERS, ANNO 1692 DEN 29 MEY EN VOLGENDE DAGEN VOORGEVALLEN.

R. de Hooge fec.

RUINEEREN DER FRANSEN OORLOG-SCHEPEN, &. TE LA HOGUE, CHERBOURG, ORNAY, &.

I   : vSt2880 FM2854 H187 R. de Hooge fec.,
      address A. D. Oossaen and P. Rotterdam,
      Amst.   39 × 56 cm
II : vSt3698 FM3889 the bottom half adapted
      for the sea-battle of Vice-Admiral Anson
      and Chef de la Jonquiere near Cape Lezard
      – May 14th 1747, address J. Hayman, Am-
      sterdam
III : vSt4077 FM4084 the bottom half adapted
      for the sea-battle near St. Malo – June 16th
      1758 (chiefly some alterations in the lower
      right corner)

I : vSt supp. FM2856a-c not signed, no address
28.7 × 40.2 cm

II : vSt2882 address Wed. J. Tangena, Leiden and
additional text

III: vSt3122 FM3358 adapted for the sea-battle near
Malaga, Spain, August 24th 1704

THE ALLIED FORCES AGAINST THE FRENCH
NEAR STEENKERKEN, BELGIUM – AUGUST 3rd
1692

vSt2898 FM2877A supp. not signed, address P. Persoy,
Amsterdam   27 × 33.5 cm

A series of thirteen prints with the address of P. Persoy
which also was published in the book by S. Gruterus (see
La87)
vSt2930 FM2905 FM2730 supp. H148 H189-H198
Title-page *Funeralia Mariae Reginae*   c.30   × 18.5 cm

Sterven der Koninginne   23 × 28 cm

172

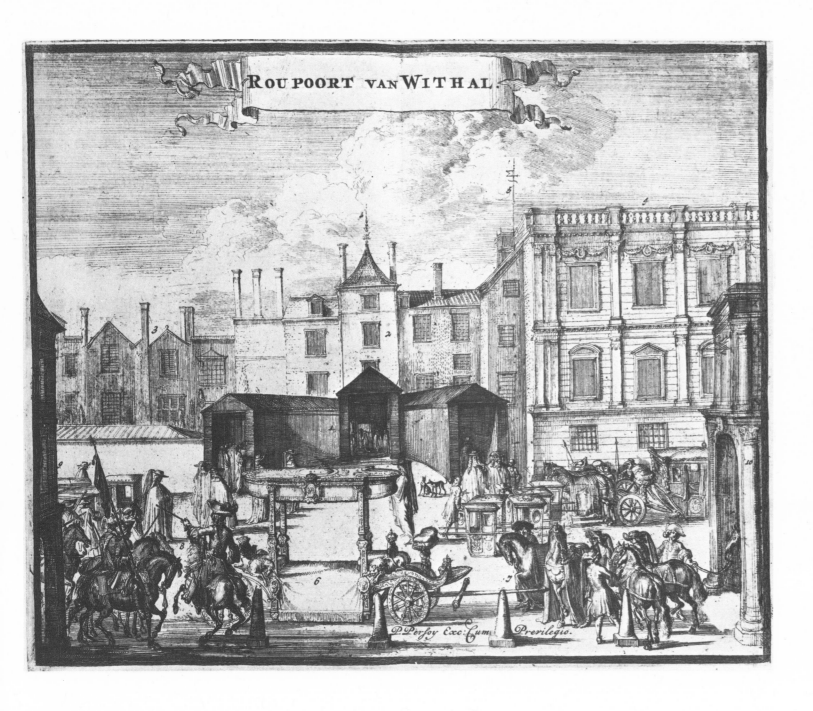

ROUPOORT VAN WITHAL

P. Perfoy Exc: Cum Prerilegio.

Roupoort van Withal   23 × 27.5 cm

173

Deathbed of the Queen   44.3 × 56 cm

BED VAN PARADE.

By Pieter Persoy met Previlegie.

Bed van Parade   23 × 27 cm

175

1. Ministri Tribuni, vulgo Marefchalchi liberum tranfi-
   rum per vias facientes, quæ fedecim pedes latæ pul-
   lato panno ftratæ, ab utraque parte eodem panno
   feptis ligneis appenfo circumfeptæ erant.
2. Lictores de viis curandis.
3. Ministri præfectorum armorum.

4. Trecentæ pauperes Feminæ lugubribus eucullis tectæ
   quaternæ incedentes.
5. Duo Tibicines.
6. Vexillum Concordiæ geftatum ab Equite Philippo
   Meadown.
7. Affeclæ, Pediffequi, Apparitores, & Ministri Oeco-
   nomici.

8. Præfecti veftimentorum & ftabuli.
9. Præfecti rei veftiariæ cubiculi.
10. Nobiles facelli & rei facræ fuo apparatu veftiti, nœnias
    cantantes per vias, ufque ad Templum Abbatiæ
    Weftmunfterienfis recepti a Præfectu Templi, cho-
    ri & facelli Henrici feptimi.

11. Duo Tibicines.
12. Cimeliarchæ. Infpectores operum, vulgo Control-
    leurs.
13. Promi condi. Prælibatores. Nobiles. Infpectores.
    Vigilum Præfecti.
14. Duo Tibicines.

Funeral procession-six leaves, each   c.22 × 56 cm

176

15. Sacellani Regis & Reginæ.
16. Scabini. Allermanni Londinenses.
17. Dominus Christophorus Wren, Archiædilis.
18. Duo Tibicines.

19. 20. Primarii Nobiles diversorum munerum Regis & Reginæ.
21. Octo horum gestantes testudinem ad funus Reginæ
  e curru delatum in templo tegendum.

22. Inter hos erant Nobiles, Fercularii, Pocillatores;
  Prælibatores &c.
23. Duo Tibicines.
24. Præfectus Armorum.

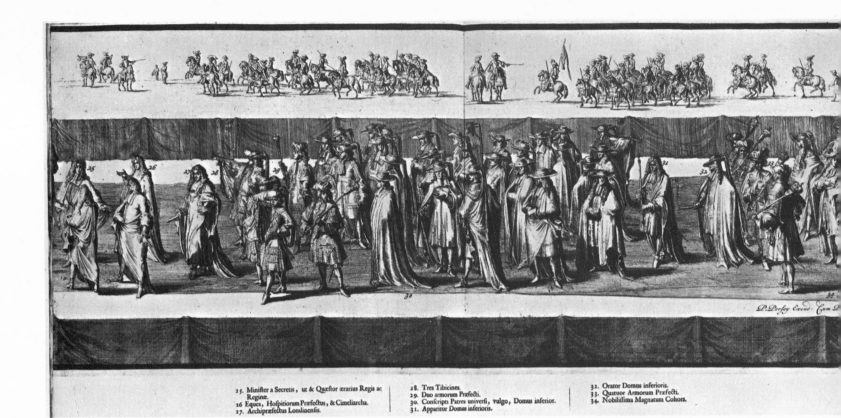

25. Minister a Secretis, ut & Quæstor ærarius Regis ac Reginæ.
26. Eques, Hospitiorum Præfectus, & Cimeliarcha.
27. Archipræfectus Londinensis.

28. Tres Tibicines.
29. Duo armorum Præfecti.
30. Conscripti Patres universi, vulgo, Domus inferior.
31. Apparitor Domus inferioris.

32. Orator Domus inferioris.
33. Quatuor Armorum Præfecti.
34. Nobilissima Magnatum Cohors.

34. Nobilissima Magnatum cohors.
35. Apparitores Ipsorum.
36. Orator Ipsorum cum referendis, vulgo de Beurs.
37. Caduceator.
38. Vexillum Ducatus Chester.   } a Magnatibus gesta.
39. Vexillum Principatus Wallis.
40. Vexillum Ducatus Cornwal.
41. Caduceator.

42. Labarum Hiberniæ.   } ostentata per Comitem Monruth & Selkirche.
43. Labarum Scotiæ.
44 45. Archicaduceatores.
46. Insignia Britanniæ Gallicis quadripartita.   } a Comitibus portata.
47. Labarum Imperatorum Monarchiæ Britannicæ.
48. Labarum Angliæ.

49. Dominus Vicecomes de Villers, Archipræfectus stabuli Regis & Reginæ, manuducens equum honorarium luctus publici, cujus caput & cauda violaceis plumis ornata erant, pullo tegmine infra ungulas demisso tectum, ac ductum a duobus stabuli Regii Ministris.
50. Caduceator Nobilis, gestans Galeam Regni, cristatam cum Diadematis apice, & Palliolo Herminarum.
51. Scutum Imperii, cum Ordine Garterii.
52. SacroSanctus Regni gladius, Curtana nuncupatus.

53. Sagum insignibus Imperii distinctum.
54. Caduceatores nobiles.
55. Clarenceaux, Alter Caduceatorum Regulus, Qui binis Nobilium Apparitoribus comitatus pulvinar violaceum &c. cui imposita Regni Diauema, Sceptra, Globus &c. ex curru Lugubri transportabat in Mausolæum.
56. Marchio de Winchester, Dom. Vice Camerarius associatus a Magnatum Apparitoribus. Hoc loco se immiscebant clerici Abbatiæ Westmonasteriensis ordini processionis, ad ipsum Ecclesiæ introitum.

57. Octo Caballi Lugubres sine veredario, manuducti a totidem Nobilibus stabulariis. Ceremoniali modo eodem, quo prior equus pompæ, adornati, Capite caudaque elatis plumis Violaceis, tegmine pullo demissiore coöperti, hi currum Augustum trahebant.
58. Sex Barones ex utraque parte Currus Augusti ostentantes Ducatuum Vexilla Scutis Regni decorata, quæ infixerunt Clausto lugubri circa Mausolæum.

59. Tres Imperii Magnates Assessores, utrinque tenentes fyrmata extrema Pallæ seu tegminis pulli, quod Augustum Funus, loculumque tegebat, cui impositum Pulvinar violaceum, Diademate, Sceptris, Globoque Britannicæ Monarchiæ coruscans. Omnes Magnates, tam Assessores quam Nobiles, lævos, humeros induti pullo linteo crispo, cæterum suis vestibus ceremonialibus vestiti.

60. Ipsa Palla, seu tegmen Lugubre, ex violaceo serico villoso, nodis aureis ac fimbriis pretiosissimis adornato, ac decoro.
61. Corona Monarchalis, Globus, Sceptra &c. pulvinari imposita.
62. A Cervicalibus ac pedibus Funeris assidentes Sacræ Majestatis Domicellæ Nobilissimæ, profundissimos luctus præ Se ferentes.

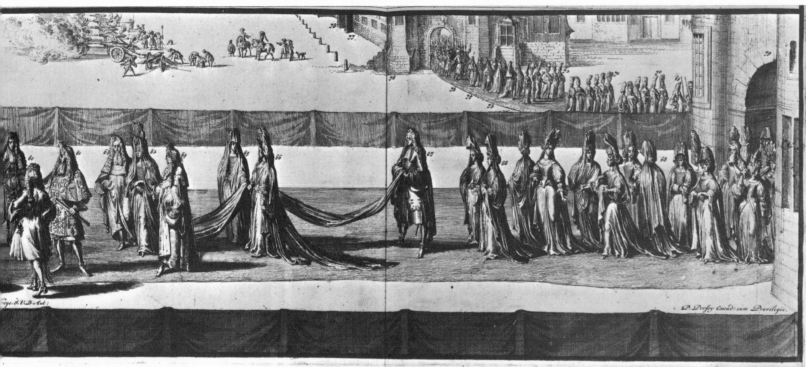

60. Duo Nobiles Magnatum Apparitores.
61. Archicaduceator, ut Caduceatorum, Scutigerorumque Regulus, Dominus Garter.
62. Primaria Pullatarum Domina Dux de Sommerset repræsentans Principem Annam Daniæ.
63.64. Dux de Leeds & Comes de Pembrock suftentantes primariam pullatarum Dominam.
65.66. Domina Dux de St. Albans. } Spatra remotiore primariæ Pullatarum Dominæ.
   Domina Dux de Southampton. }
67. Mr. Sagres Vice Camerarius Reginæ, fyrmatophorus ejusdem.
68. Octodecim Affiftentes prim. pull: Dom.

Nobiliffimæ Dominæ, Dominæ, {
Dux de Devonshire,
Comes de Bridgwater,
Comes de Winchefter,
Comes de Thanner,
Comes de Sandwich,
Comes de Radnor,
Comes de Monmouth,
Domicella Howard de Effingham,
Comes de Arran.
Dux de Leeds,
Comes de Oxford,
Comes de Northampton,
}

Nobiliffimæ Dominæ, Dominæ, {
Comes de Carnavon,
Comes de Sunderland,
Comes de Maclesfield,
Comes de Dorcheftes,
Baro Crounvel,
Lady Rockingham.
}
69. Duo Nobiles Appantores.
70. Sex Domicellæ Cubiculi Reginæ.
71. Sex Domicellæ Honorariæ.
72 Sex Fœminæ Cubiculi Reginæ.
73.74. Cohors Officialium magnorum, & Stipendiarii Nobiles.

75. Præfectus Satellitum Prætorianorum.
76. Vetus Porta Aulæ.
77. Pars Palatii Withal.
78. Porta Lugubris in Area St. Jacobi in Circuitu (de Court) Abbatiæ Weftmunfterienfis, in Area Palatii Withal, in Caftro (vulgo Tour) & alibi ex Tormentis Bellicis & Sclopetis Militum, dato Symbolo ac fignis certis, explodebatur fonitus pulveris Pyrii, luctus publici fignum undique.

181

Westminster Abbey   45.5 × 55.5 cm

PLAN VAN HET CHOOR VAN WESTMUNSTERS ABDY.

GRAFLEGGING VAN H:MAT

Gedrukt by PIETER PERSOY, Op den Dam tot Amsteldam, met Previlegie.

P.Persoy Excud: Cum Previl:

Plan van het Choor   Graflegging   23 × 28 cm

WILLEM III AND HIS FLEET NEAR
DUNKIRK – AUGUST 9th 1695

vSt2939 FM2913 not signed, no address
40 × 55 cm

184

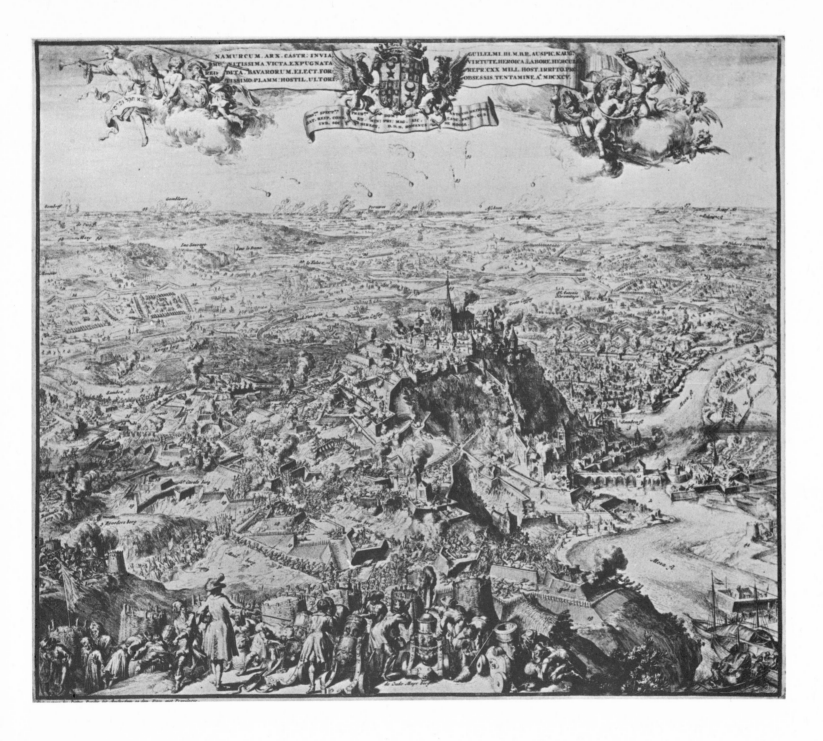

NAMUR BESIEGED AND CAPTURED BY
WILLEM III AND MENNO VAN COEHOORN –
JULY 3rd to SEPTEMBER 5th 1695

I : vSt2947 FM2934b H199 not signed, address P. Persoy,
Amsterdam   50.5 × 60.5 cm
II: FM2934c not signed, address G. Valk, Amsterdam

185

THE FRENCH GARRISON LEAVING NAMUR,
BELGIUM – 1695

I : Albertina Vienna. not signed, no address   43 × 54 cm
II: see Barcelona captured 1705 p. 199

GLORIFICATION OF THE VICTORY BY EUGENE OF SAVOYE ON THE TURKS NEAR ZENTA, HUNGARY – SEPTEMBER 11th 1697

Royal Library Brussels. Romijn de Hooghe fecit, Phi: Bouttats excudit   35.5 × 49.6 cm
Upper half of a leaf with text in two columns, divided by a small plate of fireworks.
Lit.: Georg Rósza. *Romeyn de Hooghe und die Türkenkriege in Ungarn* (Oud Holland, 1962 p. 101 ff.)

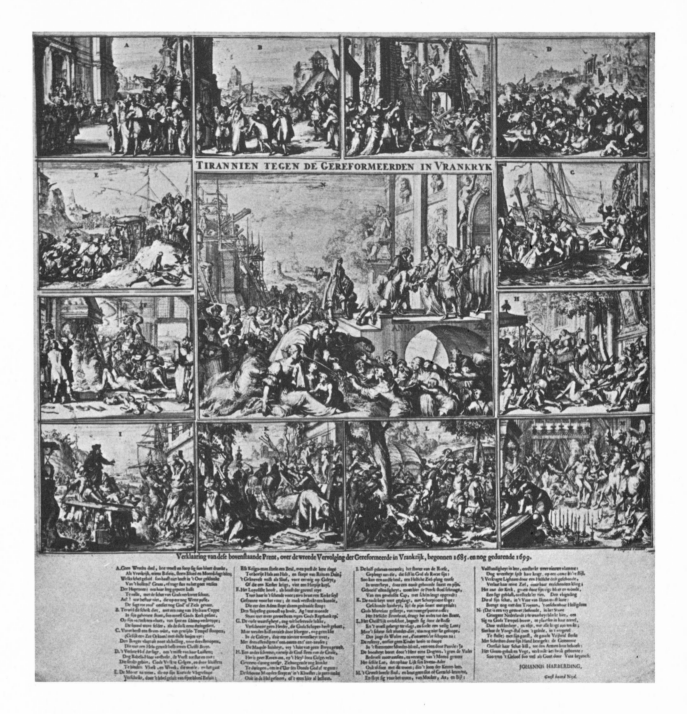

vSt supp. FM2673 H135 not signed, address I. Tangena,
Leiden   40.5 × 51 cm

vSt3055 H202 Latin dedication by De Hooghe, Ex Formis
Petri Schenk   44.2 × 60 cm

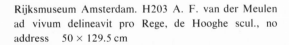

Rijksmuseum Amsterdam. H203 A. F. van der Meulen ad vivum delineavit pro Rege, de Hooghe scul., no address   50 × 129.5 cm

Entrée du Roy dans Dunquerque

le Roy entrant dans Dunquerque. 3 la fonderie .   5 L'arcenal .   7 Porte de la Ville .   9 le Port .   à la Citadelle .   12 L'Écluse .
2 La basse Ville .   4 Porte de Calais.   6 Place ou l'on bastit les Vaisseaux . 8 La grande Eglise .   10 Pont de Bois qui va de la Ville . 11 la Citadelle .   13 Les Dunes .

A. Vander Meulen, ad vivum del.

Regis in Dunkercam ingressus.

Rex Dunkercam intrans. 3. Æ des fuforio operi destinatæ .5. Armamentarium .   7 Porta primaria .   9 Portus .   11. Arx .   12 Cataractæ .

Orbs inferior.   4 Porta ad Caletes .   6 Locus navibus condendis addictus. 8 Templum majus .   10 Pons fublicius vrbem cum arce conjungens   13 Littoralæ tumuli .

I : vSt3066 FM3027 not signed, address P. Persoy,
   Amsterdam   15 × 19 cm
II: FM3027 not signed, address Wed. A. Tangena

VICTORY OF THE ALLIED TROOPS OVER FRANCE AND SPAIN NEAR LUZARA – AUGUST 15th 1702

vSt supp. FM3303 H249 R. de Hooge inv. et f., no address
48.8 × 57.8 cm

VICTORY OVER THE FRENCH BY JOHN
CHURCHILL DUKE OF MARLBOROUGH AND
EUGENE OF SAVOYE NEAR HOCHSTEDT AND
BLENHEIM, BAVARIA – AUGUST 13th 1704

I : vSt3111 FM3343a H251 Romanus de Hooghe f.,
    Ex Formis Petri Schenck, poem dedicatory to Queen
    Anna of England with chronogram   44 × 59 cm
II: see next plate

DIE DURCH HERZ:IOHANN VON VON SAVOY:BEY HOCHSTAT WIDER DIE FRANZÖSE.

I MARLBOURG · EUG DE SAVOYE

MARLBOURG UND PR:EUGENIUS UND BAYEREN ERHALTENE VICTORIE den 13 August 1704.

VICTORY OVER THE FRENCH BY JOHN CHURCHILL DUKE OF MARLBOROUGH AND EUGENE OF SAVOYE NEAR HOCHSTEDT AND BLENHEIM, BAVARIA – AUGUST 13th 1704

II: Albertina Vienna. not signed, no address   44 × 59 cm

I : see the preceding plate

195

VICTORY NEAR HOCHSTEDT AND BLENHEIM, BAVARIA – AUGUST 13th 1704

I : FM3346 H252 R. de Hooghe fecit, address Wed. J. Tangena 1704   c.15 × 19 cm

II : Teyler Museum, Haarlem with inscription "'t Dorp Bleynheijm" and some alterations

III : vSt3145 FM3428A adapted for the battle near Oudenaarden, Belgium, July 1st 1708 with the name of the etcher changed into "R. de Heigher" and with inscription "Het dorp Heine" (Belgium)

DE GLORIEUSE BATAALJE EN VICTORIE,

Bevogten op het Franfe en Keur-Beyerfe Leger by Hoogftet en het Dorp Bleynheym.
Beneffens 't gevangen nemen van den Generaal M. Tallart, en 't verdrinken der Cavallery in den Donau.

Voorleden Sondag hebbe ik my de eer gegeeven aan U Hoog Mog: te fchryven, om haer te informeeren van de refolutie die wy genomen hadden om Ingolftad te belegeren, als mede van den toeftand der vyanden: Den felven avond omtrent 11 uuren vernamen wy, dat zy den Donau by Lavingen gepaffeert waren; waar op ik middernagt den Generaal Churchil liet avanceeren met 20 battaillons, die den felven dag den Donau gepaffeert zyn om den Prins Eugenius te verfterken, en 's morgens ten 3 uuren marcheerde ik met de refte van de armee, waar van een partye (om meerder te verhaaften) de route nam van den Generaal Churchil, en de cavallerye met de eerfte linien van de infanterye paffeerde de Lech tot Rain, en den Donau by Donawaart; wy voegden ons dien felven avond by den Prince Eugenius, en campeerden met de regter vleugel tot Appertzhoven, en met de linker tot Munfter, met dat oogmerk om daags daar aan het Camp van Hogftet te betrekken; maar als den Prince Eugenius en ik het felve quamen recognofceeren met 40 efcadrons, bevonden wy dat den vyand 't felve reeds geoccupeert hadde; waar op wy de refolutie namen, op haar aan te marcheeren, gelyk wy gifteren deeden; de armee ten 2 uuren 's morgens in beweeging zynde, 't welk zy niet verwagt hadden, quamen wy ten 6 uuren in haar gefigt: tuffchen 8 en 9 begon men op malkanderen te kanonneren; maar terwyl de vyanden 2 beeken met een moeras voor haar hadden, foo moeft de cavallerye defileeren, en den Prins Eugenius een groot retour doen, en was het wel 2 uuren des namiddags eer men hadgemeen koft werden: De vyanden formeerden zich in 2 corpfen, den Keurvorft en de Heer Marfin aan de flinker, en Monfr. de Tallard met alle fijne troupen aan de rechter vleugel; deefe laatfte viel my te beurt: Eyndelyk begon het gevegt te verheffen, en duurde tot Sonnen ondergang, wanneer het God behaagde aan de Geallieerden te verleenen een feer groote en volkomen victorie; de bravoure van onfe troupen, en van de Generaals, Officiers en foldaten is niet uyt te drukken, en meriteeren den grootften lof die men haar geven kan: zynde de cavallerye geobligeert op het chargeeren vier a vyf maal te retourneeren; maar den tyd laat my niet toe een detail te geeven; haar gantfche armee is in route geflagen; wy hebben een feer groote flagtinge gedaan, en hebben haar campement met al het kanon en munitie ingenomen; aan myn kant hebben wy meer dan 30 efcadrons in den Donauw gedreeven, alwaar wy het grootfte gedeelte hebben fien verdrinken, en maakten den Heer Tallard met feer veel van fijne Generaals en Officieren gevangen. In het dorp Bleynheim, welk de vyanden verfterkt hadden, hebbe ik 26 battaillons en 12 efcadrons al op difcretie gevangen bekomen, boven dat hebben wy een feer groot getal van ftandaards en vaandels verovert. Ik weet noch het volkomen detail niet van het gepaffeerde op de regter vleugel, maar de goede conduite van den Prince Eugenius, en de bravoure van fijne troupen eclateren byfonderlyk in deefen gelukkigen dag, waar mede ik niet hebben willen wagten U Hoog Mog: te feliciteeren, latende het refteerende aan den Colonel Panton, een van myn Adjudanten Generaal, die geweeft zynde in de actie, U Ho: Mo: de particulariteyten mondeling fal bekend maken.

Waar mede,   Hoog: Mog: Heeren, &c.

Uyt het Campement van Hogftet den 14 Augufty 1704.

Getekent,
LE DUC DE MARLEBOROUG.

Gedrukt tot Leyden, by de Weduwe van J. Tangene. 1704.

TRIOMPH of ZEEGEN-KOETS,

Van de Hoog Mog: Heere Staten Generaal der Vereenigde Nederlanden, op de Glorieuſe

Batalje en Overwinning van de Hoge Geallieerden, tegen de Franſe en Beyerſe,

voorgevallen by Hoogſtet en Beynheym den 13. Auguſti 1704.

at vrees'lijk naar gekerm, geſugt, ge-
    klaag, geween?
Doet *Tiphon*, die *Juno*, drie-tant en
    ſlang door een;
Vervult met d'Echo van ſijn rampſpoet
    en elende;
Hy die *Jupyn* wel eer deed' zidd'ren, met
    ſijn benden
Vol hoogmoed, legt geveld! geſlagen, door de kragt.
Der Goden! *Hanibal* die met ſijn oorlogs magt
Oud *Romen* ſelfs beſtreed, is met *Carthagoos* wallen,
Door dapp're *Schipioos* ter aarde neer gevallen!
Schoon *Polikrates* was hoogmoedig door 't geluk,
Orontes met ſijn heir brengt hem in angſt en druk.
't Fortuyn en 't zonne rad is als *Seſoſtrus* rad'ren,
Het geen de *Licaöns* en *Phaëtons* doed nad'ren
    Aan *Styks*, of *Lethes* ſtroom: 't Blijkt aan dien wrede Vorſt
Die als een *Mar'jus* of *Golinus*, heeft getorſt
't Bevel van heir en volk, maar onvernoegt, t'onvrede,
Verraat, verwerpt, beſtrijd ſijn vrinden; ja die wrede
    Dorſt, tragt, haakt na 't genot van Schepter, Rijk en Kroon
    Van d'*Ad'laar*, voor die geen die namaals hem den loon.
Laſthemes geven ſal, ſiet *Atrop*, *Hama* ſtromen
Na d'eeuw'ge ziele plaats, wilt *Nikouws* volk vry ſchromen,

U Vorſt is weg gevlugt, ſijn heir ter neer geveld,
    Ja dertig duyſend man gedood, of in 't geweld
Van ons zeeg'-pralend' heir! *Tallard* u hulp gevangen,
Met vyftien hoofden van ſijn volk! ſingt vreugde ſangen
    Gy *Ad'laar*, *Diſtelbloem*, *Harp*, *Roos* en moed'ge *Leeuw*,
    Nu de verſtrikkers ſelfs verſtrikt zijn, hoor 't geſchreeuw
Vol vreugt in *Hollands* tuyn, van 't ſtarre dak weergalmen,
D'wijl dat de Goden tolk *Merkuur*, ſtrooyt vreugde palmen;
    De *Leeuw* die d'vryheyt met *Apollos* vier-geſpan,
    En d'ſeve pyllen voerd', komt met de *Faam* nu van
Germania in praal, bevragt met d'opper helden,
Met ſlang, mirt, lauw're bekroond, om dat ſy moedig ſtelden
    Haar leven in 't gevaar; aanmerkt de ſeven aan,
    't Vereenigt *Nederland*, die d'hoogmoet van den *Haan*,
Met d'afgodin de nijd, vertreeden en weerſtreven.
Lang moet ons ov'righeyt met onſe helden leven;
    By wien *Minerva* blinkt, gelijk de gulde zon;
    En *Aſtrea* regeert, den hemel die een bron
Vol zegen uytſtort op ons Land en onſe Staten,
Door wiens genadt dat den vyand moeſt verlaten
    Het veld, 't geſchut en al de ſtandaarts, die tot buyt
    Bekomen zijn, waar door de *Faam* nu overluyt
Uyt blaaſt, dat in geen eeuw ſoo 'n ſlag en is geſlagen,
Daar d'lauwer kroon ſoo groot, ſoo heerlijk is gedragen!

Gedrukt tot *Leyden*, by de Weduwe van *J. Tangena*. 1704.

FM3357 H253 Roma: de Hooghe fecit, address Leyden,
by de Weduwe J. Tangena 1704   c.11 × 16 cm

VICTORIES BY THE ALLIED FORCES OVER THE
FRENCH – 1704

Museum Boymans-Van Beuningen. vSt3124 FM3365 not
signed, address P. Schenk, Amst.   48.8 × 59 cm

198

VEUE DE BARCELONE DU CÔTÉ DE LA MER.

II: Albertina Vienna. FM3378 not signed, text-leaf with
the address D. de la Feuille   43 × 54 cm

I : see The French garrison leaving Namur 1695 p. 186

1674	Siege of Grave, Holland	ex 1673 Siege of Naarden, Holland
1675	The titular duchy of Gelre offered	ex 1674 Utrecht rejoining the Union
1690	Coronation of Joseph I of Hungary in Augsburg	ex 1674 Coronation of John III of Poland in Cracow
1690	Sea-battle near Bevesier, England	ex 1673 Sea-battle of de Ruyter
1690	Battle near the Boyne, Ireland	ex 1678 Campaign on the isle of Rugen
1691	Siege of Athlone, Ireland	ex 1689 Londonderry, Ireland
1691	Victory at Slankamen, Hungary	ex 1687 Victory at Nagyharsány, Hungary
1693	Battle near Landen, Belgium	ex 1674 Battle near Seneffe, Belgium
1693	Battle near Neerwinden, Belgium	ex 1689 Battle near Walcourt, Belgium
1697	Peace-treaty at Rijswijk, Holland	ex 1678 Peace-treaty at Nijmegen, Holland
1702	Queen Anna in Parliament, London	ex 1689 Willem III in Parliament, London
1704	Sea-battle near Malaga, Spain	ex 1673 Sea-battle of de Ruyter
1705	Capture of Barcelona, Spain	ex 1695 The French garrison leaving Namur
1708	Battle near Oudenaarden, Belgium	ex 1704 Victory near Hochstedt, Bavaria
1709	Battle near Bergen, Belgium	ex 1674 Battle near Seneffe, Belgium
1710	Battle near Zaragoza, Spain	ex 1690 Battle near the Boyne, Ireland
1720	George II in Parliament, London	ex 1702 Queen Anna in Parliament, London
1747	Sea-battle near Cape Lezard	ex 1692 Sea-battle near La Hogue, France
1758	Sea-battle near St. Malo	ex 1692 Sea-battle near La Hogue, France

See also 1675 Battle near Aschaffenburg p. 93

	vSt	FM	H
PLATES ARBITRARILY ATTRIBUTED TO DE HOOGHE			
Map of the mouth of the river Thames	—	2270b	—
Chatham or Rochester ... signed: A. de	2356	2255a	75
Siege of Namur	—	2928 supp.	—

HISTORICAL PRINTS

1188 DAMIATE see inset page 337

1572/3 SIEGE AND RELIEF OF HAARLEM see inset page 337

1574 SIEGE AND RELIEF OF LEYDEN

See further also LA 45, 91, 102.

References: H F. W. H. Hollstein. *Dutch and Flemish Etchings. Engravings and Woodcuts.*

Volume IX. Amsterdam 1953

FM F. Muller. *De Nederlandsche geschiedenis in platen.*

Amsterdam 1863-1882. 4 vols. (Reprint: Amsterdam 1970)

vSt G. van Rijn. *Atlas van Stolk.*

Amsterdam, 's-Gravenhage 1895-1931. 10 vols. *Index.* 's-Gravenhage 1933

I : vSt532 FM672c + supp. H63 Before the coins in the
    upper corners, not signed, on text-leaf address J.
    Tangena; right lower corner "Landschyding"
    42.5 × 46.8 cm
II : vSt533 FM672a Coins in the upper corners, Romijn
    de Hooghe fecit, address J. Tangena, right lower
    corner "Landschyding"
III: the same as II but signed Romijn de Hooghe fecit et
    excudit also in Pierre van der Aa. *La Galerie Agreable
    du Monde,* no date
IV: Coins in the upper corners, signed Rom de Hooghe
    fecit, no address, right lower corner "Land scheiding"
V : the same as IV but unsigned

POLITICAL
CARICATURES

1674   THE STATE OF WAR WITH FRANCE:

After Poland's King died (November 10th 1673) and before Wilhelm of Fürstenberg was

arrested (February 16th 1674)

FRENCH ALLIES THWARTING PEACE:

A French party and Fürstenberg trying to thwart peace-negociations between France, Munster

and Cologne, at Cologne

DE KUYP AEN DUYGEN: Wilhelm of Fürstenberg arrested

MISLUCKTE PAPENKRYGH EN DE FRANSCHE VERHUYS-TYDT:

The war between France and the Republic 1672-1674

1684   THE DISCORD BETWEEN AMSTERDAM AND WILLEM III:

d'Avaux trying hard to set Amsterdam against Willem III

1687   KONING – SPEL COURANT OP 'T JAER 1687 – see page 144

1689   JAMES II AND LOUIS XIV:

Arlequin Deodat, et Panurge Hypochondriaques

Arlequin Furieux et Pantagion triumphant

Arlequin sur l'Hypogryphe ala Croisade Lojoliste

La belle Constance dragonée par Arlequin deodat

l'Epiphane du Nouveau Antichrist

l'Europe Allarmée pour le fils d'un Meunier

La Feste des Trois Rois, aux Invalides

Les Monarches Tombants

Panurge secondé par Arlequin Deodat à la Croisade d'Irlande

Paye qui tombe

Qualis vir, Talis Oratio

POLITICAL CARICATURES

1689   JAMES II AND LOUIS XIV:

De Vlugt van 't Pausdom uit Engelant

Wie boven zynen staet, verwaent zich durft verheffen

1690   THE STRIFE BETWEEN AMSTERDAM AND WILLEM III:

– Nieuw liedt van de driedubbelde kruysvaert van de ridders

– Mardi Gras de Cocq a l'Ane

Pantagruel Agonisant

1701   Esopus in Europa – see LA95

1702   'T GESEEGEND JAER VAN MDCCII:

The Emperor of Austria opening Carlos' II testament

References: H   F. W. H. Hollstein. *Dutch and Flemish Etchings. Engravings and Woodcuts.*

Volume IX. Amsterdam 1953

FM   F. Muller. *De Nederlandsche geschiedenis in platen.*

Amsterdam 1863-1882. 4 vols. (Reprint: Amsterdam 1970)

vSt   G. van Rijn. *Atlas van Stolk.*

Amsterdam, 's-Gravenhage 1895-1931. 10 vols. *Index.* 's-Gravenhage 1933

Lit.:   C. van de Haar. *Romeyn de Hooghe en de pamflettenstrijd van de jaren 1689 en 1690.*

Groningen 1956. Tijdschrift voor geschiedenis. Vol. 69, pp. 155-171

ALLEGORY ON THE STATE OF WAR
WITH FRANCE – 1674

I   : vSt2571 FM2519 H109 Romeyn de Hooge
      Fecit, no address   26.5 × 40.8 cm
II : vSt3315 FM3183 adapted to the situation
      of 1709 but published in 1711, signature
      erased, address: Te Love by Melman
III : vSt3316 FM3181 *Wigs en Toris-Balans*,
      inscriptions altered, the same address as II

I : vSt2578 FM2528 H161 not signed, no
address   24.5 × 35 cm
Compare with next plate

II: FM2770 *Het Stookhuis der Princen deses
Tijds, in Europe* … adapted to the situation
in 1689

III: vSt2767 in second state, compare with the
    preceding plate   24.5 × 35 cm
IV: vSt3223/24 FM3099-3100 *Door Kryg
    vermoeyde Europa's Vorsten* (from the
    same plate), adapted to the situation in
    1706; plate and verses on separate leaves

DE KUYP AEN DUYGEN,

vSt2577 FM2525 H110 nog signed, no address
23.8 × 34 cm

For a small copy see LA41

MISLUCKTE PAPEN KRYGH,
en
DE FRANSCHE VERHUYS-TYDT,

Uijtgespeelt op de Roomsche Heijlige Dagen.

Van kers-nacht tot Meij Dagh.

vSt2595 FM2521 not signed, no address
33.7 × 45.6 cm

Vette Koe van Farao gy moet weeten . Dat gy van de magere kunt werden gegeeten Marlais .f.

vSt2705 FM2668 + supp. H138 Marlais f.,
fictitious address with text   17 × 26.5 cm

Arlequin Deodat, et Pamirge Hypochondriaques.

Wee riep den Doctor, sulk gespuys
Moet na het Dol en gecken buys:

Ick heb noch vry vat te geneesen
Eer alles op syn stel sal wesen.

Gisling f: et exc: Geneve.

I : vSt2763 FM2754 H154 Gisling f. et exc. Geneve
34 × 38.5 cm
II: vSt3351 FM3205 inscription *'t Verbeter-huys der Torys*... with chronogram (1713) but without the name of Gisling

213

I : vSt supp FM2755 H155 not signed, no address
  27.3 × 39 cm
II: with address: Anvers chez C. C. Boudats

Arlequin fur l'Hippogryphe ala Croisade Lojoliste.

vSt2805 FM2756 H156 not signed, no address, Dutch
verse 33.6 × 38.4 cm

La belle Constance dragonée par Arlequin deodat.

Gisling Geneve f. d exc.

I : vSt2802 FM2757 H157 Gisling Geneve f. et ex. Dutch
verse   34.2 × 38.2 cm
II: FM2757 b The same, with Dutch verse and French
version

L'Epiphane du Nouveau Antichrist. 1689

I : vSt2768 FM2759a H158 with inscription, not signed
33.7 × 38.4 cm
II: FM2759b without inscription, not signed

CARICATURE OF JAMES II AND LOUIS XIV – 1689

L'Europe Allarmée pour le fils d'un Meunier.

vSt2746 FM2760 not signed, no address   33.5 × 37.5 cm

218

La Feste des Trois Rois, aux Invalides.

vSt2769 FM2761 H159 not signed, no address   34.2 × 36.2 cm

vSt2807 FM2762 not signed, no address   33 × 39 cm

Panurge secondé par Arlequin Deodaat.
a la Croisade d'Irlande. 1689.

I : vSt2815 FM2766a H160 not signed, no address
    33.5 × 39.2 cm

II: vSt3658 FM3846 adapted for the defeat of Charles
    Edward Stuart, Colloden 16 APRIL 1746, address:
    Wed. J. van Egmont Amst.

Qualis vir Talis Oratio

vSt2750 FM2767 not signed, no address   33.2 × 38 cm

DE VLUGT VAN 'T PAUSDOM UIT ENGELANT.

Wie boven zynen staet, verwaent zich durf verheffen,   *Verdient, ten spiegel van verwaenden aanst, ten toon*
En steeken overdwaas den Hemel naar zyn Kroon.   *Te staen op een schavot, en ramp op ramp te treffen.*

AG Sant LOUIS, waer berg ik my
Voor 't naken quaad? Ai staat my by!
Of ik ben met het lief 't jong KINDJE
Capot, en ligter als een windje.
Al onsen aenslag is mislukt,
En 't geen my nog het meeste drukt,
'k Sie my van vreemde magt besprongen,
En van myn eigen volk gedwongen,
Om af te staen, 't geen ik voor heen
Sogt t'onregt met de voet te treen.
Ik wil het doen, en 't staat te dugten,
Of 'k egter niet sal moeten vlugten.
Kunt gy dan Santus PETRUS niet
Afbidden, die aenstaend verdriet?
Men prepareert voor Uw jong Lammetje
Wat anders, als een liefslijk prammetje.
Schoon den BEKEERDER maakt getier,
En hier en daar het Oorlogs vier
Ontsteekt, en nog wat maekt bravade.
't Kan my niet helpen van mijn schaede.
'k Vrees Hy krijgt mů nog eens sijn loon
Voor 't schricklijk tergen van de Goon,

Voor 't woeden, en 't tirannisieren;
Eylaes, hoe kan de kans verkeeren!
Ik sie, te laat, vast tot myn schand,
Dat wie sig tegens God aenkant,
En Hamans lust heeft ingeloopen,
't Ook met sijn straffe moet bekoopen.
O ROME wyt van roem en waerd,
Hoe komt gy eindlijk dus ontaerd,
Dat Gy, met Uw twee liefste Soonen,
U laet besporten, en dus hoonen.
Sijn dan Uw' blixems die voorheen
Soo meenig Keiser boven deen,
Geblust? of is de tyd gekoomen
Van d'ondergang van 't magtig Romen.
Doe ik met reen dan niet beklag,
Dat ik vervloek die uur en dag,
Doen ik Uw' staetzugt en Uw' leere
Omhelsfden, met een vol begeere?
Wat sal men na mijn ondergang,
Van my al maeken meenig sang?
Na gy my dus laet in de peckel,
Is 't seeker, MENE, MENE, TEKEL!

vSt supp. FM2773 not signed, no address   34 × 38.5 cm

Nieuw Liedt, van de drie-dubbelde Kruyfvaert
van de RIDDERS en GROOTEN
uyt uythangborden gefprooten.

I : vSt2823 FM2792a H163 not signed, no address
   16.7 × 25 cm
II: vSt2824 FM2792b caption in two lines

Mardi Gras de Cocq, a l'Ane.

FRANSE KAEL-ENDER,

Beginnende vander Onnoofele Kinderen-dag 1689. tot de Borgers Goe-Vrydag A° 1690.

1. Barsse Jan begon te woelen,
In 't fat gefelschap op de Doelen,
En riep, hoe kittebroers, ons meesterschap loopt gevaer,
Krakeelen wy niet met malkaar;
Den Baes is uyt, wy konnen 't drayen
Dat onfen Haen fal meester kryen,
'tSa Borsjes, feyd hy, feg je gront,
Mit vloogen drie vier op, en roerden flout haer mont,
Sullen wy als *Onnofle Kinderen*
Ons fo verminderen,
Wy fijn foverain, en boven alle wetten,
Wy kennen niemant, en die hem tegen ons wil fetten,
Daer fet hom onfe vrient, die dollen Haen
Mee tegen aen,
't Is nu juyft *Nieuwe Jaer*,
Sla nu de handen in malkaer,
Sluyt maer je beurs, wat raeckt ons een ander,
Sijn wy niet, grove achtbaer, machtig en schrander?
En hebben op ons zy
De Borgery.
2. *Drie Koningen*, fijn op onfe hand
Wel opgeleeren,
En op den Grooten Baes gebeeten,
Siet mannen wat, een vafte band
Op *Coppermaendag* flack de jongfuls vaen na buyten,
De meefte part rinkelrooyde als fot,
En dreyg'de als een Libourlot,
Het Jonkers hof fig al die muyten,
't Was al hy fal on moeter uyt,
Die in onfe kaert kijckt, en 't fpul verbruyt.
De hoop was, dat men van die noble baefen
Wel yemant vinden fou, die mee begon te raefen,
Dat mifte, en de heele buyrt
Waer tegen hem, wel opgeguert.

3. Doe flonk het leelijk, want men de banken moeft ftellen
In 't Recht huys, en dat werk begon te koellen.
5. *Vrouw-lichtmis*, dat is, rieper een' mijn funótie,
Men kent my voor een helt
In 't velt
Als Mars en Venus in conjunctie,
Elck fette doe fijn knevels op
De blicken draeyden in de kop
Van al het brullende, Collegie
't Was, Vreede, Vryheyt, Privilegie.
Maer Religie, daer dogt niemant om,
Want dat fucht niemant voor eygendom.
Privilegien, riep een daer moetmen niet of reppen
Of onfe Borgers moeften de Brantklock kleppen,
En daegen ons voor de Deur
Om het heur.
Hoemen 't difeyde, 't was mis, en de kraem in duygen,
Niemant wou het recht, na heur driften buygen,
't Was *Quatertemper*, de naefte Saturdagh,
In 't gelagh.
Om dat Wijtheyt en Reeden,
En fachtheyt van feeden,
Van wackere mannen,
Quam famen te fpannen,
En flatte de Vaert
Van 't hollende Paert.
4. *Vaften-avond*, moeft de mafquers noch patroüilleeren
De Speelman, fiegde op in 't Frans
En Hollebeurs quam aen den Dans:
5. Men hoorde Rommel-pot en grof Papou braveeren,
Al ftondenfe alle dry in 't Hemd,
So wien de reden en fatfonnicheyt overftemt.
6. Daer klonken Sinter Claes Louyfen.
7. Ha! Riep de dollen Franfen Haen,

Daer fpeur ik de Oude Vrienden aen
Die fo voor de Vryheyt fpreekt, moetmen prijfen,
Hy riep vaft, om fijn hert benout,
Siet vrienden die op mijn vertrout
Die ftaet voor eeuwig vaft, juyft fat de guijt en Kackte
En vergde vaft fijn Poort aen Seegels en Contracten,
Hy had fijn Kamer ftoeltje net
Op al fijn Vrientjens huyd gefet,
Die wierden vroeg of laet bedreeten.
8. Garde vous, riep fijn Vroutjen droef bekreeten,
Sy liep als een Beedelerfter fonder kap, fonder keurs,
En fonder beurs.
Afdag over al! Wie fal mijn armoe decken,
9. *Partifans*, Malrotiers en Intendanten trecken,
Soldaten, Beuls en Papen, moorden, ftraffen en flien,
10. *Vrienden* en Vyanden, fietmen na de Galeyen gaen:
De *Vaften* die ons opgeleyt werd, fal eeuwig duyren
En al die ook fo licht betrouwen lang befuyren,
11. *Quatertemper* en *Botreff* riepen de Hoeren van 't Hof,
't Moet alles of.
Juweelen, Servilen, en Koftelijke kleeren
Moetmen aen de Soldaten, facrinceeren
So fulje mee vieren, fo jy ons Hoofd
In 't flicktloyen geloofd
Maer blijf Eenig en Trou, fo fal 't haeft *Goe-Vrydag* wefen,
De *Donkere Meffen* falmen leefen
Wanneer Oranje, de gedrochten verjaecht,
Waer van de Borgers fijn geplaecht.
Sie Grootsheyt en Gierigheyt moeten betalen,
12. Want wat de Sog mifdoet, komt men van de Biggen halen.

Tot Antwerpen, By CORNELIS WOONS, op de Mekk-
Mart, in de Gulde Sterre. 1690.

vSt2825 FM2793 H164 not signed, address: Antwerp,
C. Woons 1690   37 × 39.2 cm

227

vSt2847 FM2816 H167 Guindeau inv. J. Marlais f. a
Londres with Dutch and French verse
26.5 × 34.6 cm

vSt3093 FM3304 not signed, no address   47.5 × 57 cm

PLATES RETOUCHED

FOR SUBSEQUENT EVENTS:

1689 The state of Europe   ex 1674 French allies thwarting peace
1706 The state of Europe   ex 1674 French allies thwarting peace
1709 The state of war   ex 1674 The state of war with France
1713 *'t Verbeter-huys der Tories*   ex 1689 *Arlequin deodat*
1717 Whigs and Tories   ex 1674 The state of war with France
1746 Defeat of Charles Edward Stuart   ex 1689 *Paye qui tombe*

PLATES ARBITRARILY

ATTRIBUTED TO DE HOOGHE:

		vSt	FM	H
1672	*Bericht van den hemel aan den koning*	2422	2332	—
1672	Allegory on the death of the de Witts … Decker f.	2483	2432	—
1674	*Anticurius van Loevesteyn*	2573	2523	—
1674	*De dood van het Eeuwig Edict*	2574	2524a	83
1674	Caricatures of France, Cologne and Munster	2586	2536	—
1674	Dream of the Bishop of Munster	2588	2537	—
1677	Funeral of Dom. Johan van de Velde	2656	2618	—
1687	*Requiescant in pace*	—	2690b	—
1689	*Sic itur ad astra* … William Logan f.	3281	2765b	
1692	*Desolaten inventaris*	2890	2862	188
1701	*Alarm te Versailles, of Spinhuis* … Ph. B(outtats)	3162	3047	247
1702	*Vygos cagados* … monogram NR	3082	3295	—
1702	*De Ban en Arrier – ban*	3083	3296	248

PORTRAITS

Contemporaries: Matthijs Balen, see LA 45

Carlos II of Spain

Carlos III of Spain

Christian IV of Denmark, see page 116

Ysbrand van Diemersbroek

Maria Beatrix d'Este

Servatius Gallaeus

Willem Joseph van Gendt, see de Ruyter page 251

John III of Poland – two prints, see also page 77 and 126/127

Don John of Austria

Joseph I of Hungary, see also page 143

Jules Mazarin, see LA 12

Franciscus Mollo and Anna Maria Ooms

Johan Baptista Neercassel

Adriaan Pauw

Martinus Pauw

Karel Rabenhaupt

Michiel Adriaensz de Ruyter, see also under Mausoleums

Willem Bastiaensz Schepers

Cornelis Tromp

Johan van de Waeyen

Willem III – six prints, see also pages 89, 90, 98, 114, 115, 119, 122, 151, 164

Willem III and Mary Stuart see page 258

Cornelis de Witt

Cornelis and Johan de Witt, see also pages 63, 64

Ludwig von Wolzogen

PORTRAITS

Don Manuel Lopez de Zunega

PLATES RETOUCHED

FOR OTHER PORTRAITS:

1704	Carlos III of Spain	ex Carlos II of Spain
1688	Joseph I of Hungary	ex Lopez de Zunega
1689	Willem III	ex Joseph I of Hungary
1705	Carlos III of Spain	ex Willem III

References: H   F. W. H. Hollstein. *Dutch and Flemish Etchings. Engravings and Woodcuts.*
Volume IX. Amsterdam 1953

fm   F. Muller. *Beschrijvende catalogus van 7000 portretten van Nederlanders en van buitenlanders tot Nederland in betrekking staande.*
Amsterdam 1853

s   J. F. van Someren. *Beschrijvende Catalogus van gegraveerde portraiten van Nederlanders.*
Amsterdam 1888-1891. 3 vols.

vSt   G. van Rijn. *Atlas van Stolk.*
Amsterdam, 's-Gravenhage 1895-1931. 10 vols. *Index.* 's-Gravenhage 1933

FM   F. Muller. *De Nederlandsche geschiedenis in platen.*
Amsterdam 1863-1882. 4 vols. (Reprint: Amsterdam 1970)

LA   J. Landwehr. *Romeyn de Hooghe* (1645-1708) *as book illustrator. A bibliography.*
Amsterdam, New York, 1970

I : vSt3106 per Romanum de Hooghe, address J. Leonard
    Brussels   57 × 48.4 cm
II: see page 236

A fine example of the preceding plate retouched

II : vSt3106 per Romanum de Hooghe, address erased,
    head removed
I : see page 235
III: see page 237

236

III: vSt3106 FM3329 H250 per Romanum de Hooghe,
address N. Visscher, poem by F. Kaarsgieter
57 × 48.4 cm

YSBRAND VAN DIEMERSBROEK –
Professor of medicine at Utrecht

vSt portrait 203/19 H378 fm 1310 Romeyn de Hooghe
des. J. Edeling sc.   42.2 × 28.5 cm

238

MARIA BEATRIX D'ESTE – Consort of James II of Scotland

Teyler Museum not signed, no address   27.6 × 21.6 cm

SERVATIUS GALLÆUS ROTERODAMENSIS BATAVUS.

Heus! GALLÆVS hic est, procul hinc tot Dæmonis artes.
Ficta Sibyllarum, tempora fata, fides.
Vna Via est; Nihil Orcus habet: Vir Strenuus anteit
Dum Gallo – Batavos, Servat alitq̃ Fide .

posuit, R. de Hooge . 1686 .

H379 fm 1783 R. de Hooge 1686   26.2 × 17.9 cm
Also in *Dissertationes de Sibyllis* – LA 72
I : before the words *opt de Dei…*
II: as reproduced

240

JEAN III. avant SOBIESKI, Roi de Pologne.
a Leide. Chez Pierre vander Aa.

H390 signed Romanus de Hooghe fec. et inv. 1674
sumptibus Fr. Gratae   48.3 × 69 cm
A small copy: Fr. Grata S.R.M. Polon, secr. delin.,
address: Pierre van der Aa, Leiden   26 × 35.5 cm

JOHN III OF POLAND – circa or after 1674

Albertina Vienna. not signed, no address   48.5 × 39.5 cm

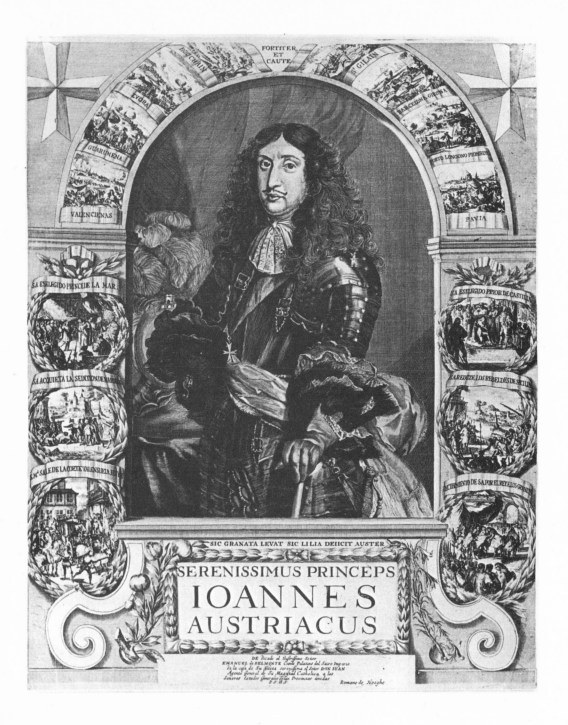

SIC GRANATA LEVAT SIC LILIA DEIICIT AUSTER

SERENISSIMUS PRINCEPS
IOANNES
AUSTRIACUS

DON JOHN OF AUSTRIA – The Chief Spanish Commander

H381 Romanus de Hooghe with dedication to E. de Belmonte   52.5 × 42.5 cm

JOSEPHUS.I.D.G. REX HUNGARIÆ

II : Albertina Vienna. R. de Hooge fec. 1688
48.6 × 67.5 cm
I : see portrait of De Zunega p. 265
III/IV: see portrait of Willem III page 261

244

ALLEGORY ON THE MARRIAGE OF
FRANCISCUS MOLLO AND ANNA MARIA
OOMS – 30TH SEPTEMBER 1674

vSt2605 FM supp. *2567A* H383 not signed, no address,
dedicated to Jeronimus Parensi and Nic Andrea Jensini
48.2 × 39.1 cm
Lit.: J. Koenen. *Geschiedenis der Joden in Nederland,*
p. 219

JOHANNES BAPTISTA NEERCASSEL –
Papal nuntius

ILLUSTRISSIMUS ac REVERENDISSIMUS D.D. IOANNES NEERCASSEL EPISCOPUS
CASTORIENSIS ET PER FOEDERATUM BELGIUM
VICARIUS APOSTOLICUS

QUI. CUM. ECCLESIAS. SUAS.   OMNIBUS. AC. SINGULIS.
PRECIBUS. CONCIONIBUS. ELEEMOSYNIS.   AMORE. MODERATIONE. PATIENTIA.
EFFUSIS. PROFUSIS.   SEMPER. GRATISSIMUS.
FORMAVERAT. FIRMAVERAT. AUXERAT.   DEO. OPT. MAX. TAMEN. GRATIOR.
RELLIGIONIS. PIETATIS. SAPIENTIÆ.   SUIS. BEATAM. MEMORIAM. SUI.
PER. SEMILUSTRUM.   ALIENIS. DESIDERIUM.
EXEMPLAR.   RELIQUIT.

M. S.

ANNO 1686. 6. IUNI OBIIT.

H384 fm 3818 after C. Braau Harlemi   46 × 35.6 cm

ADRIAEN PAUW, RIDDER, HEER VAN BENNEBROECK, SCHAECKENBOS, ETC. PRÆSIDENT OVER HOLLANT, ZEELANT. EN VRIESLANT.

H385 fm 4125a not signed   45 × 33.8 cm

H386 fm 4126 Romanus de Hooghe… 1682
59.5 × 43.7 cm

CAREL R   BENHAU
Baron van Such?, &c. Heer   Lichtenberg en Fremes
Heere van Crumbagh General   Lieutenant der Vereenigde
Landen, Collonel over een Reg   ment Infanterye, Governeur van G
gen en Omlanden, Castelyn va   Coeverden, en Dreyfaart van Drenth

T Amsterdam, by Kornytaus Sweerts, op his Dam inden Venbowen Hoek, 1673

H387 not signed, address K. Sweerts Amst. 1673
35 × 29 cm

249

I : vSt supp. s 4711 H388 address Romeyn de Hooghe,
   Amsterdam. With separate text   46.2 × 35 cm
II: Prentenkabinet Leiden. address Joannis de Ram (Am-
   sterdam)

THE ADMIRALS MICHIEL ADRIAENSZ DE
RUYTER AND WILLEM JOSEPH VAN GENDT –
1667

FM2275 very likely by De Hooghe   c. 33 × 26 cm

WILLEM BASTIAENSZ SCHEPERS –
Admiral and burgomaster of Rotterdam

H389 s 4887 not signed, no address   47.4 × 36.5 cm

ADMIRAL CORNELIS TROMP – 1673
(after the third sea battle)

CORNELIS TROMP.
Lt Admirael, Van Hollandt,
en West Vries Landt,
uytgegeven tot Amsterdam bij ROMEYN d. HOOGHE.

I : vSt supp. H391 address R. de Hooghe, Amsterdam
     46.3 × 34.5 cm
II : fm 5418 address: H. Allardt (Amst.)
III: Teyler Museum Haarlem. With medal on the ribbon

253

I : H392 s 6034 before the letter   36.1 × 28.4 cm
II: as reproduced

vSt2440 H393? uytgegeven by Romeyn de Hooghe
t'Amsterdam   51 × 40.3 cm

WILLEM III – circa 1672

Albertina Vienna. H395 s 327 Romeyn de Hooghe, no
address   48 × 43 cm

I : vSt supp. FM2381 Aa supp. R. de Hooghe f., address
M. Doornick Amst. Willem III *without* hat
46.9 × 56.8 cm

II : vSt2443 FM2381 Ab supp. before inscription and
before address Doornick. Willem III *with* hat

III: vSt2443 address Doornick Amsterdam. Willem III
with hat as reproduced

ALLEGORY ON THE CORONATION OF WILLEM
III AND MARY STUART

I   : vSt2794 FM2737b H152 R. de Hooge, address:
      C. Allard, Amst. genealogical tables, with verse by
      L. Smids   36.7 × 37 cm
II : Without genealogical tables, address C. Allard (Amst.)
III : vSt2794 with the address of Karel Allard (Amst.)

Albertina Vienna. not signed, no portrait
45 × 63 cm

I : vSt2791 FM2724a + supp. H145 R. de
Hooge Delineavit et Fecit, address: J. de
Ram   37.5 × 61 cm
before the letter. *The only mezzotint by
De Hooghe*

II: FM2724 with the letter, poem by J. Norel
and the personification of Holland with
slightly different attributes

WILHELMUS. III. D. G. MAG.
BRIT. FRANC. ET. HIB. REX &

III: vSt2843 FM2811 + supp. not signed, J. Tangena
(Leiden 1689) plate cut at left   c.49 × 57.5 cm
For first state see Don Manuel de Zunega, second
state see Joseph I

IV: FM3379 „De derde Carel ... in Spagnien". J. Tangena
(1705). Retouched e.g. monogram replacing coat of
arms

I : vSt2367 FM2276 and supp. not signed, no
    address   47 × 68 cm
II: signed R. de Hooghe, address:
    A. Schoonebeek

Leven en Doot van Mr. JOAN DE WIT, raet penfionaris van Hollant en Weft-vrieflant, en fyn Broeder CORNELIS DE WIT, oudt Burgermeefter van Dordrecht, en Ruart van den Lande van Putten, om 't Leven gebracht den 20 Augufti 1672. in 's Gravenhage.

vSt2474 Portrait of Johan de Witt by Lambert Visscher, the remainder by Romeyn de Hooghe   52 × 38 cm
Below the brutal assault, The Hague August 20th 1672
see also pages 62, 63, 64

LUDWIG VON WOLZOGEN – Professor of theology
at Utrecht

H396 fm 6237 R. de Hooghe f. A° 1687   37.4 × 28.2 cm

264

EL EX.º S.º
DON MANVEL LOPEZ DE ZVNIGA
DVQVE DVQVÉ DE BEGAR Y PLAZENCIA &

I : Teyler Museum Haarlem. Johannes Ledes-
ma ad vivium delineatum d.d.d. Romanus
de Hooghe auct et inv. no address
c. 49 × 67.5 cm

II: see portrait Joseph I of Hungary

MAUSOLEUMS

Maria Bartensleben

Christophe von Kannenberg

Michiel Adriaensz de Ruyter

Albertina Vienna. not signed, no address   46 × 39 cm

MAUSOLEUM OF CHRISTOPHE VON KANNEN-
BERG – General of the Elector of Brandenburg

Teyler Museum Haarlem, not signed, no place
47 × 39 cm
Von Kannenberg was married to Maria Bartensleben, he
died February 10th 1673

I : vSt2652 FM2607a H126 before Romanus de Hooghe
    Auctore underneath   52.5 × 41.5 cm
II : vSt2652 Romanus de Hooghe Auctore underneath
III: FM2607b explanatory text and dedication to the
    Admiralty of Amsterdam by De Hooghe

HISTORICAL PERSONS

LA 93

Arrianus Alexandrinus	Philip Melanchton
Johannes Buchold	Thomas Munzer
Johannes Calvin	Nestorius
Donatus Eutyches	Nicolaus
Georgius Iconolatra	Theophrastus Paracelsus
Emperor Henri IV	Photius Iconoclasta
Hildegardis	Paulus Samosatenus
Johannes Hus	Hieronymus Savonarola
David Joris	Caspar Schwenckfeld
Julianus Apostata	Menno Simonsz
Macedonius	Theodor Sutor
Mahomat	Paulus Thebanus
Majorinus Numida	Jacobus Zonzalus
Manes	LA 93 | 100 Martin Luther

TOPOGRAPHY

Maps: ENGHIEN see page 315*ff*

GASCOGNE

THE MEDITERRANEAN

GRONINGEN – PROVINCE (for the city see page 61)

HAINAUT see page 319

HOOGHEEMRAADSCHAP RIJNLAND (1687)

IRELAND see page 165

MARSTRAND see page 113

OOST INDIEN

POLAND see pages 76 *ff*

PAVIA

SAVOYE AND PIEDMONT

UTRECHT

Views: ALDENBIESEN and twelve castles of the German Order of Knighthood (1700)

ALKMAAR – Market and city weigh-house (1674)

AMSTERDAM-Plan

Profile from the land-side

Profile from the sea-side

The new Portuguese Synagogue – eight prints

The old Portuguese Synagogue

The house of Mr. Dacosta

The house of Mr. Belmonte

The house of Mr. De Pinto

Funeral in the Jewish cemetary

(Ouderkerk aan de Amstel)

AMSTERDAM – Funeral rites in the Jewish cemetary

(Ouderkerk aan de Amstel)

ARNHEM – Annual Fair

BREDA – view of the castle, see pages 56, 57

BRUSSELS see pages 132 *ff*

CLEVES-PRINSENHOF – Bird's eye view, profile etc. – eleven prints

DIEREN – Arrival of Willem III king of England (1691)

DORDRECHT – View and plan, see LA 45

ENGHIEN – Bird's eye view, profile etc. (1685) – twenty one prints

HAARLEM – Plan and profile (1688-1689)

THE HAGUE – see LA 1, 19, 79-81

HONSELAARSDIJK – see LA 79-80

HOORN – see LA 104

LINGEN – Seminary

LISBON

LONDON – see pages 154-159, 171 *ff*

HET LOO – Bird's eye view, profile etc., and eight drawings of statues

MIDDAGTEN see page 304

MONT MELIAN (1675)

OSNABRUCK – see LA 4/23

PADERBORN – see LA 4/23

ROTTERDAM – Plan, profile etc., see also LA 3

SALZDAHLEM

TOPOGRAPHY

Views: TURIN – three prints

VILLA ANGIANA see ENGHIEN

Castles of the German Order of Khighthood: ST. AEGIDIUS

               ALDENBIESEN

               BECKEVOORT

               BERNSHEIM

               DE BIESEN

               JUNGE BIESEN

               GEMERT

               GRUYTROOY

               LIEGE (ST. ANDREAS)

               ORDINGEN

               RAMERSDORF

               ST. PIETERVOEREN

               ZEESTORFF (= SIERSDORF) ... see page 282

Garden Architecture: see Cleves, Enghien, Het Loo and Salzdahlem

References: H   F. W. H. Hollstein. *Dutch and Flemish Etchings. Engravings and Woodcuts.*
Volume IX. Amsterdam 1953

FM   F. Muller. *De Nederlandsche geschiedenis in platen.*
Amsterdam 1863-1882. 4 vols. (Reprint: Amsterdam 1970)

vSt   G. van Rijn. *Atlas van Stolk.*
Amsterdam, 's-Gravenhage 1895-1931. 10 vols. *Index.* 's-Gravenhage 1933

LA   J. Landwehr. *Romeyn de Hooghe* (1645-1708) *as book illustrator. A bibliography.*
Amsterdam, New York, 1970

Amsterdam University L. R. de Hooghe f., address Gerard
Valk Amsterdam   46 × 55 cm
in *Atlantis sylloge compendiosa … or nova totius geo-
graphia telluris projectio.* (Amsterdam, G. Valck en
L. Schenk c. 1702)

273

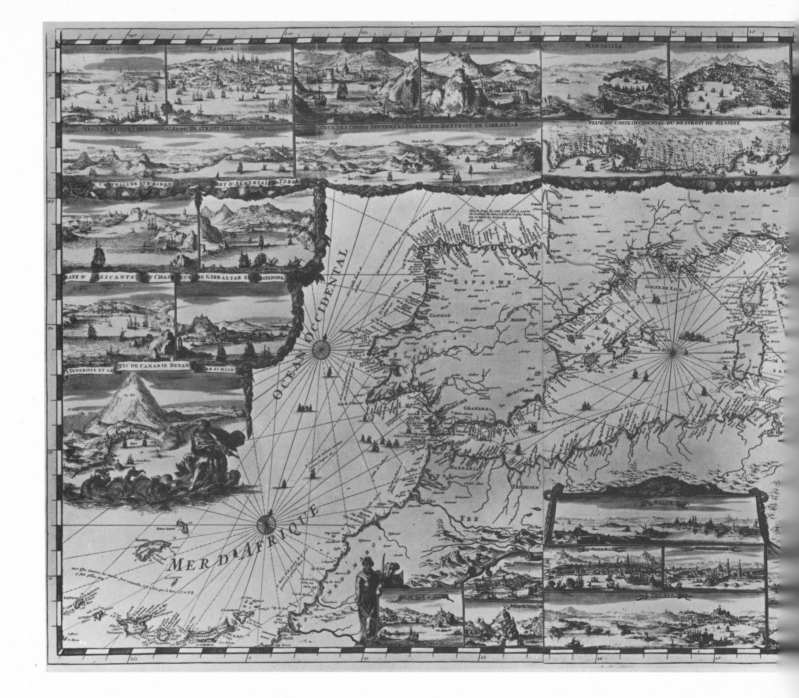

Algemeen Rijksarchief The Hague, reference: Leupe
1368. H129

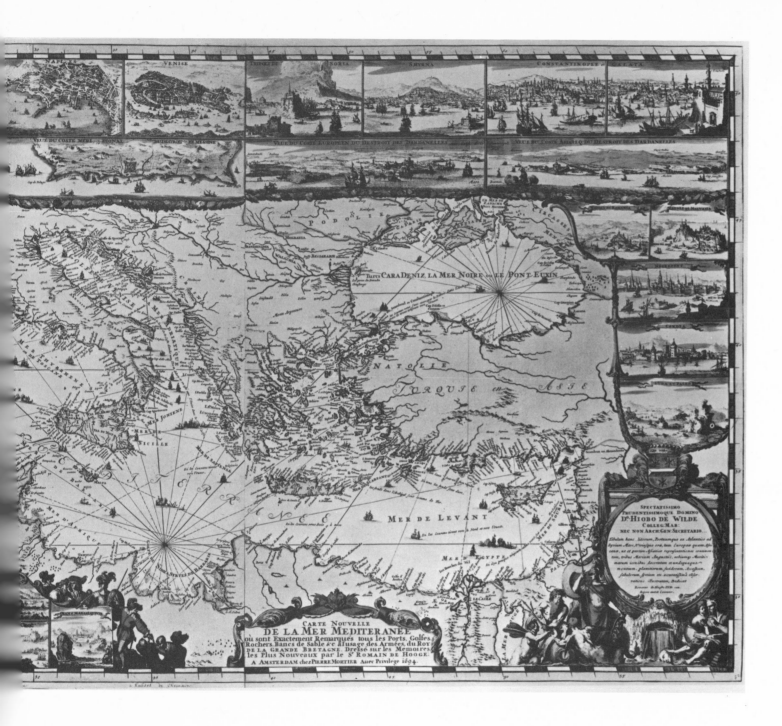

signed: R. de Hooghe, address Amsterdam P. Mortier, 1694   c. 58 × 140.5 cm

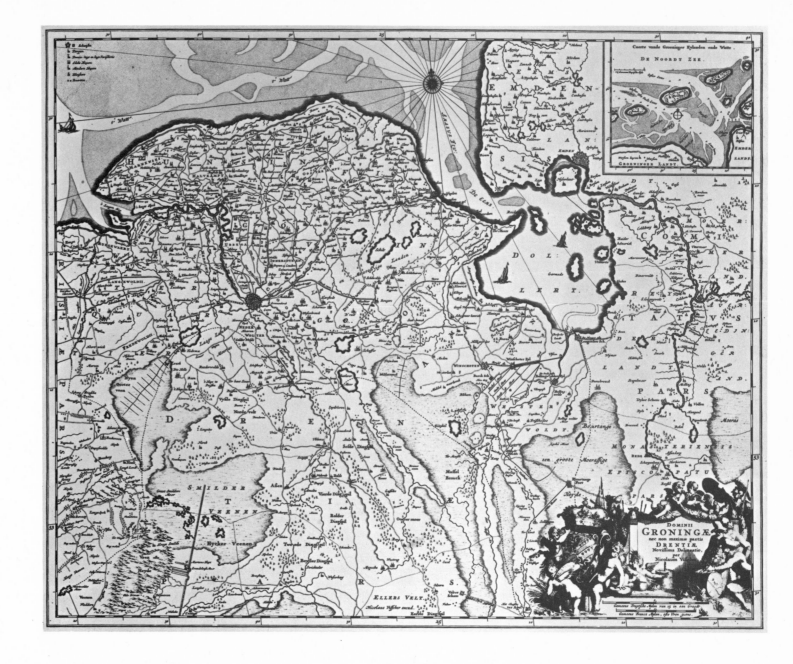

Amsterdam University L. R. de H. f., address N. Visscher
(Amsterdam)

Second edition of the map by Jan Jansz. Dou and S. van Broeckhuysen now augmented with borders by Romeyn de Hooghe   215 × 243 cm

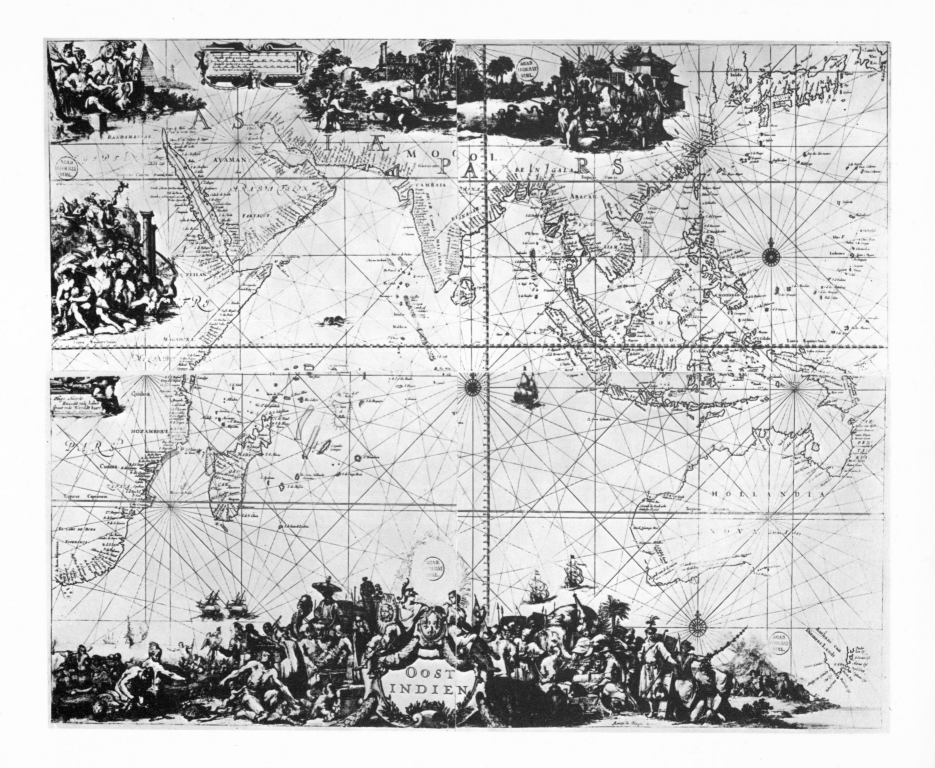

Leyden University Library Romijn de
Hoghe four leaves   c. 70 × 90 cm

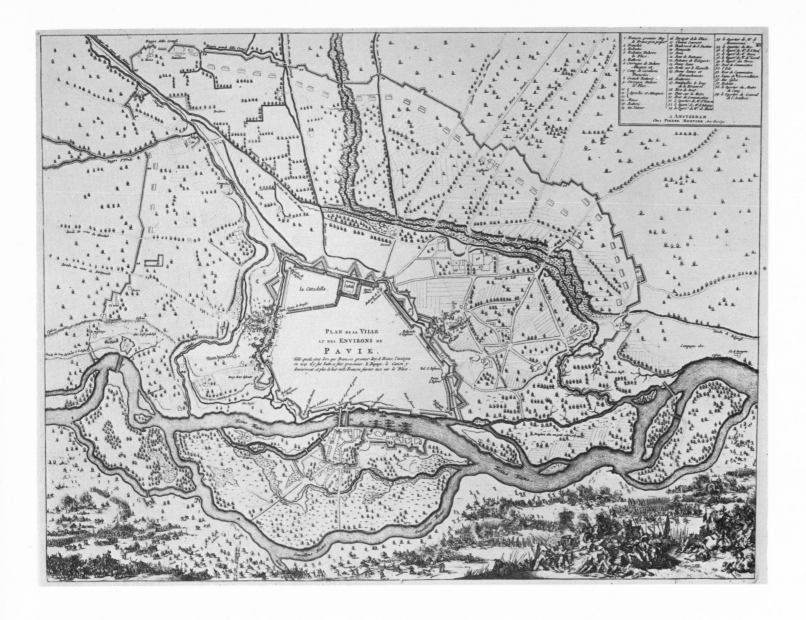

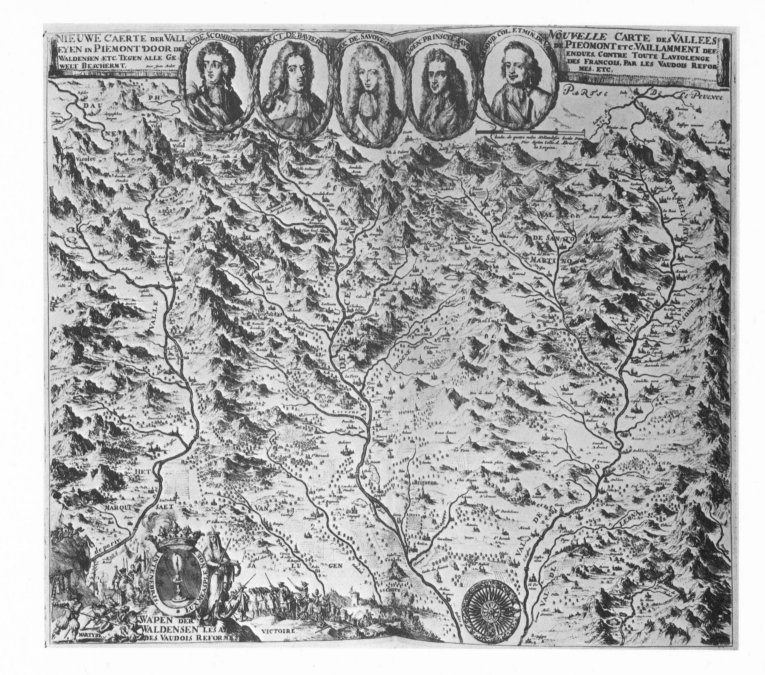

Albertina Vienna. not signed, no address   c. 47.5 × 56 cm

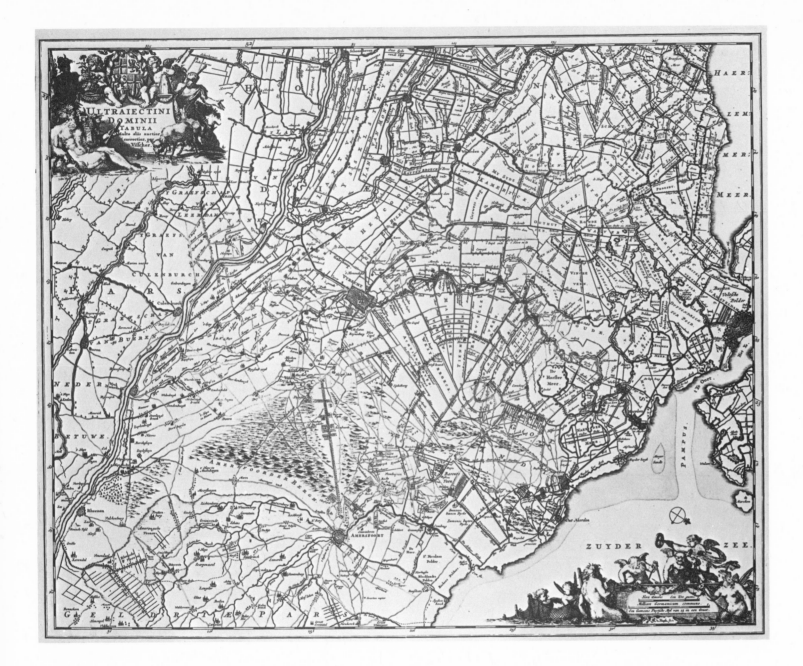

Amsterdam Library University R. de Hooghe fecit,
address N. Visscher (Amsterdam)   46 × 57 cm
also in *Atlas minor sive geographiae compendiosa …*
Amsterdam, N. Braakman 1706

Bailiwick Utrecht. H254, 323, 328, 334, 342 auct Romano
de Hooghe, no address   135 × 100 cm
lit: M. Kossmann. *Een zeldzame prent van Romeyn de
Hooghe.* (*Oud Holland* 1951, pp. 186-189)

I : vSt2042 FM3007 supp. H255 before in-
scriptions and data, except ,,Anno 1674''
41.5 × 62 cm
II: Teyler Museum Haarlem, with data, in-
scriptions, address: Adriaen Hasersou ...
... (Alkmaar) has been carrying on trade for
years, it is provided with a super abundant
cheese market and it frequently holds
markets in cattle, horses, and other
business...

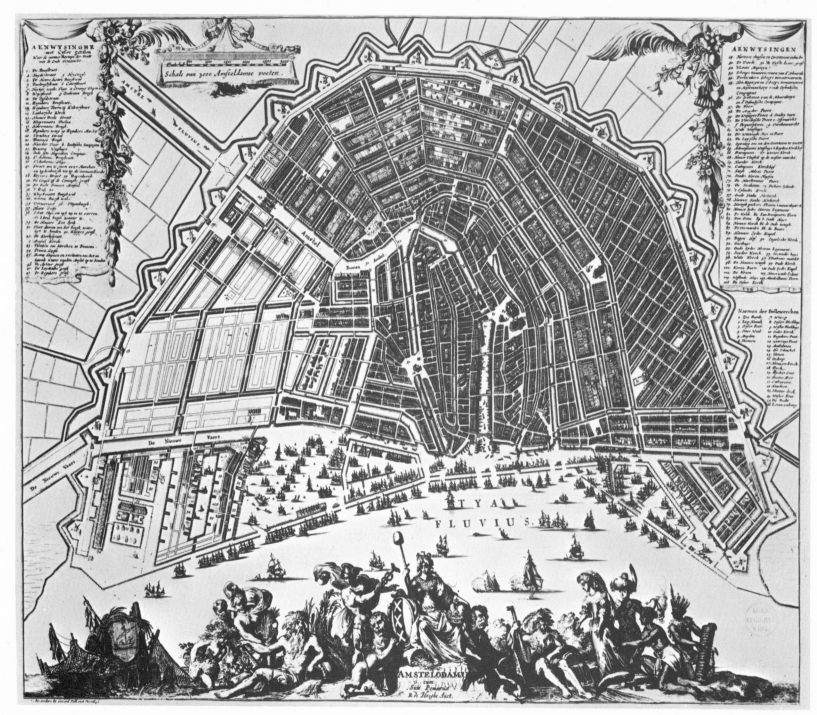

Leyden University R. de Hooghe Auct., Amsterdam
G. Valk   46.5 × 56 cm

PROSPECTUS URBIS A PARTE TERRESTRI

A. E. d'Ailly. *Repertorium van de profielen der stad
Amsterdam:* no. 112 15.7 × 55.7 cm
*...The East India House, its wharf, stores and warehouses
are almost as wonderfully grand and excellent as those of
the Board of Admirality; no close-packed forest could
compare with the Y full of masts...*

A. E. d'Ailly. *Repertorium van de profielen der stad Amsterdam:* no. 113 (with text)   13 × 55.4 cm
...In Holland – expecially in Amsterdam or Rotterdam – one often sees, during the week, the auction of the Dutch East India Company and at the same time two or three loadings of ships from Smyrna or from America to the amount of seven and eight million, all manned within eight or ten days...

T PROFIL VAN DE KERK

PLATTE GROND DES KERKS

H116 not signed, no address   23.1 × 56.6 cm
*...The Jews also enjoy an excellent and ready reception;
they are great merchants who trade to the Mediterrenean,
the Levant, Spain, Portugal and the whole of Asia and
America... They have two proud churches there, one for
the Spanish and one for the Portuguese Jews*

AMSTERDAM – THE NEW PORTUGUESE SYNAGOGUE INAUGURATION AUGUST 2nd 1675

I : H117 FM2574A Amsterdam Auctore Romano de Hooghe, with text in Dutch, Portuguese and French, a Portuguese sonnet by D. L. de Barrios, a Hebrew sonnet by S. d'Oliveira, a sonnet in Dutch, Latin and Portuguese by the etcher, with his address: Kalverstraat, Amsterdam   39.1 × 49.7 cm

II : Amsterdam Auctore Romano de Hooghe, address of F. de Widt (Amsterdam)

III: in: *La célèbre ville d'Amsterdam*. Leiden, P. van der Aa, no date. The address of De Widt erased

I : Albertina Vienna. not signed, address above: Peter
    Persoy, below „Met Previlegie..."   46 × 55.5 cm
II: vSt supp. FM2574B supp. H118 not signed, address
    J. Danckerts (Amst.)

vSt2619 H118 (see also LA 43) not signed, no address
38 × 30.6 cm

DE PREDIKSTOEL EN BINNEN TRANSEN
Nieuwelyks uytgegeven door Pieter Persoy op den Dam met Privilegie

not signed, address: Pieter Persoy   22.8 × 27.5 cm

AMSTERDAM – THE NEW PORTUGUESE
SYNAGOGUE

not signed, address: Pieter Persoy   22.8 × 27.4 cm

VOORHOF EN INGANG DER VRO...

Pieter Persoy exc.

not signed, address: Pieter Persoy   22.8 × 27.5 cm

AMSTERDAM – THE NEW PORTUGUESE
SCHOOL etc.

not signed, address: Pieter Persoy   23 × 27.7 cm

DE GEWEESENE KERK DER IODEN
Nieuwelicks uytgegeve door Pieter Persoy met ...

H256 not signed, address: P. Persoy   22.6 × 27.8 cm

H257 not signed, address: Pieter Persoy   21.9 × 27.1 cm
*...Here the churches are simple but the houses of the
burghers are beautiful; in other countries the houses are
poor and the churches are rich...*

HOF VAN DEN BARON BELMONTE
Nieuwelycks uytgegeven door Pieter Persoy met Privil

H258 not signed, address: Pieter Persoy   22.7 × 27.8 cm

H259 not signed, address: Pieter Persoy   22.5 × 27.3 cm

H260 not signed, no address   23.4 × 28 cm

FUNERAL IN THE JEWISH CEMETARY
(OUDERKERK AAN DE AMSTEL)

H261 not signed, no address   23.4 × 28 cm

300

Iaarmarckt buyten Arnhem

vSt3040 FM3013 supp. R. de Hoog fecit, no address
46.2 × 55.6 cm
…*Arnhem is situated in the heart of Guelders between
Nijmegen and Zutphen, half an hour from Ysseloord on
the Rhine, it is a graceful sight as it lies in a wooded area
and the air is healthy*…

PRINSENHOF AND GARDEN AT CLEVES 1685 / 1695

A series of 11 etchings which can be assembled to one plan measuring circa 105 × 110 cm; it consists of 2 profiles, a bird's eye view and 8 numbered plates. Some etchings bear the coat of arms of Arnold van Wachtendonck and Anna Theodora van Wendt. The series in first state has not yet turned up. In second state reference is made incorrectly to the Castle of Middachten. Some references to Cleves were changed e.g. Kermisdal becomes Issel. In third state references were changed to Cleves and the hair style of the *fontanges,* en vogue in 1680-1690, is no longer depicted.

Lit.: *Gorissen* – Fr. Gorissen. *Conspectus Cliviae. Die klevische Residenz in der Kunst des 17. Jahrhunderts.* Cleves 1964. pp. 90-91, plates 95, 97-106

VEUE DES TERRASSES, AU DESSUS DE LA RIVIERE L'ISSEL, VERS LES MONTAGNES. | Gesigt van de Terras, over de Rivier den Ysel, naa het Gebergte.

- *Gorissen 105*/106 not signed, no address
  19.7 × 52.5 cm
  II: as reproduced, with monogram of
  Wachtendonk – Wendt

VEUE DE LA MAISON ET DES JARDINS EN PROFIL
Gesigt van 't Huis en Tuinen in Profil.

- Gorissen 105/106 not signed, no address
  20.2 × 52.5 cm
  II: as reproduced

VEUE GENERALE DE LA ... MAISON, DES JARDINS, ET DES PLANTAGES DE LA ... SEIGNEURIE DE MIDDAGTEN. Generaal gefigt van 't Huis ... Tuinen en Plantagien van de Heerlykheit ... Middagten.

– Gorissen 97 H273 (= H322)
II : with the wrong name of Middagten, address Haerlem... Johan Tangena, signed Romyn de Hoogh 41 × 53.3 cm
IIa: the same, without signature/address – as reproduced
III: inscription: „La Cour ou le Chateau de Clèves... Het Princenhof..." address: Amsterdam chez Henri de Leth...

VEUE DU COTE DE KERMISDAEL
VERS LES TERRASSES.
Gesigt van de kant van de Kermisdael
na de Terrassen.

Gorissen 98
II : Albertina Vienna. Veue du cote de l'Issel…
     Gesigt van den Ysel-kant   20 × 26.1 cm
III: With inscription as reproduced and some more
     hatching

- Gorissen 99
II : Albertina Vienna. the lady left with *fontange*
   19.8 × 26.3 cm
III: the lady left without *fontange* as reproduced

VEUE DE L'ALLEE DERRIERE LE GRAND JAR
DIN ORNEE DES STATUES ET DES ORANGERS
Gesigt van de Laan agter de Groote Tuin verciert
met beelden en Orangie bomen.

– Gorissen 100
II : Albertina Vienna. the ladies on the stairs and right
    below with *fontange*   20.4 × 26.6 cm
III: the ladies on the stairs and right below without
    fontange as reproduced

307

VEUE DE L'ORANGERIE, ET DES
Gesigt van de Orangerie, en broey backen.

Gorissen 101 H272
II : Albertina Vienna. the two ladies on the terrace and a
   third on the right with *fontange*   c. 20.5 × 26.7 cm
III: the two ladies on the terrace and a third on the right
   without *fontange* as reproduced

NEUE DU GRAND PARTERRE DERRIERE
LA MAISON.
Gesigt van t Groote Bloemperk agter het Huis

– Gorissen 102
II : Albertina Vienna. the ladies at left and at right near
the vase with *fontange*   20 × 26.3 cm
III: the ladies at left and at right near the vase without
fontange as reproduced

VEUË DES ENTRÉES, ET DE LA PLAINE DEVANT LA MAISON.
Gesigt van de ingangen, en t'Plein voor't Huis.

Gorissen 103
II : Albertina Vienna. the lady at the right with *fontange*.
    20.3 × 26.2 cm
III: the lady at the right without *fontange* as reproduced

LE PETIT VERGIER AVEC CES BER:
CEAUX &c².
De Cleene Bogaart met desselfs lust
Prieelen etc.

– Gorissen 104

II : Albertina Vienna. the lady near the right corner of the
hedge and in the window with *fontange*.
20 × 26.2 cm

III: the lady near the right corner of the hedge and in the
window without *fontange*

de S^t.saanen Tooren

Laag Elten   Hoog Elten   Greethuysen

la Riviere de Kermisdaal.

VEUE AU LONG DE LA RIVIERE DE
KERMISDAAL VERS LA MAISON.
Gesigt langs de Rivier de Kermis-
daal naar d'Huis

8

– Gorissen 95

II : Albertina Vienna. Veue an long de… l'Issel… Gesigt
     langs de … Ysel   19.8 × 26.3 cm

III: With inscription as reproduced and additional
     hatchings

312

Aensomst van syne Kon: Maj: van Groot
Brittannien, op Dieren.

HIC LEO NASSAVIUS

...GIS PROTECTOR ET ...

Adventus Magni Guilielmi III Britann:
Regis in Dieram.

vSt supp. FM2838 H186a not signed, no address
44.7 × 58.5 cm

313

ENGHIEN AND ITS PARK

De Hooghe etched for 2 publishers:

1.1 Bird's eye view in two leaves for Nicolaes Visscher, Amsterdam.

1.2 A series of 17 etchings, numbered A to R and dedicated to Philip Charles Duke of Aremberg, to which was added a pamphlet consisting of 14 pages (the last with impressum of N. Visscher). Plate D is dated 1685

2.1 A profile for Johannes Tangena, Leiden.

2.2 Bird's eye view with a descriptive pamphlet of six pages entitled: ,,PLATTEGROND. En opgeligte, Bouw, Plant en Scheer-werken van het onweergadelijke Lust-perk van ENGUIEN, Gelegen aen de Stad Enguien, tusschen Brussel en Bergen in Henegouwen, nevens de Gesigten der bysonderste aenmerckelijkheden, Fonteynen, Allëes, vreemde en Inlandsche Gewassen, Bloemen, Boomen, etc. Tot genoegen der Liefhebbers op nieuws over en na gesien, met de veranderingen die in 't geseyde Perk aengeleyd en volbragt zijn. Met privilegie. Tot Leyden, by Johannes Tangena".

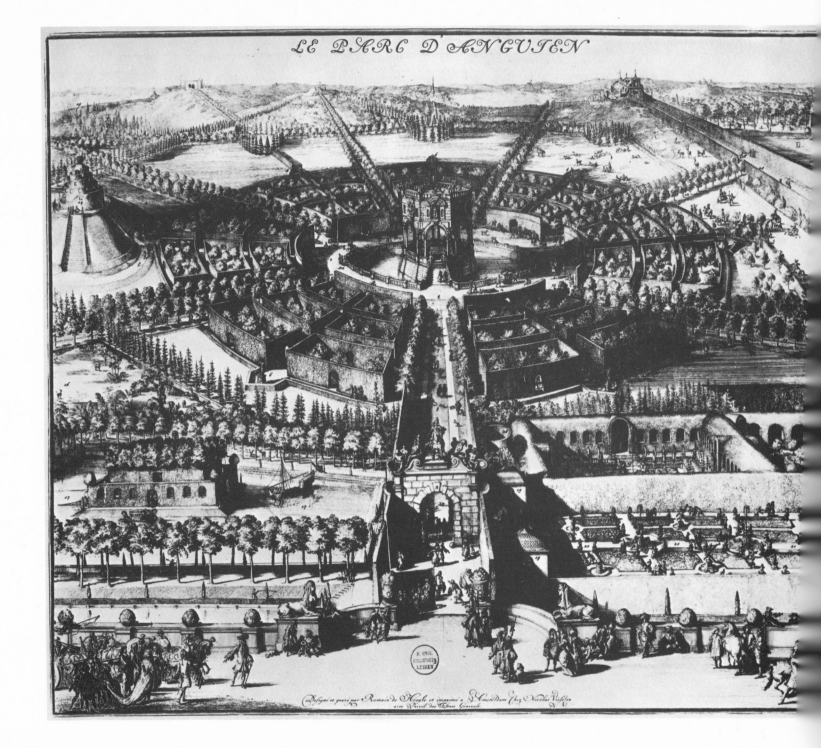

LE PARC D'ANGUIEN

Designé et Gravé par Romain de Hooghe, Amst.
N. Visscher   46.5 × 57 cm

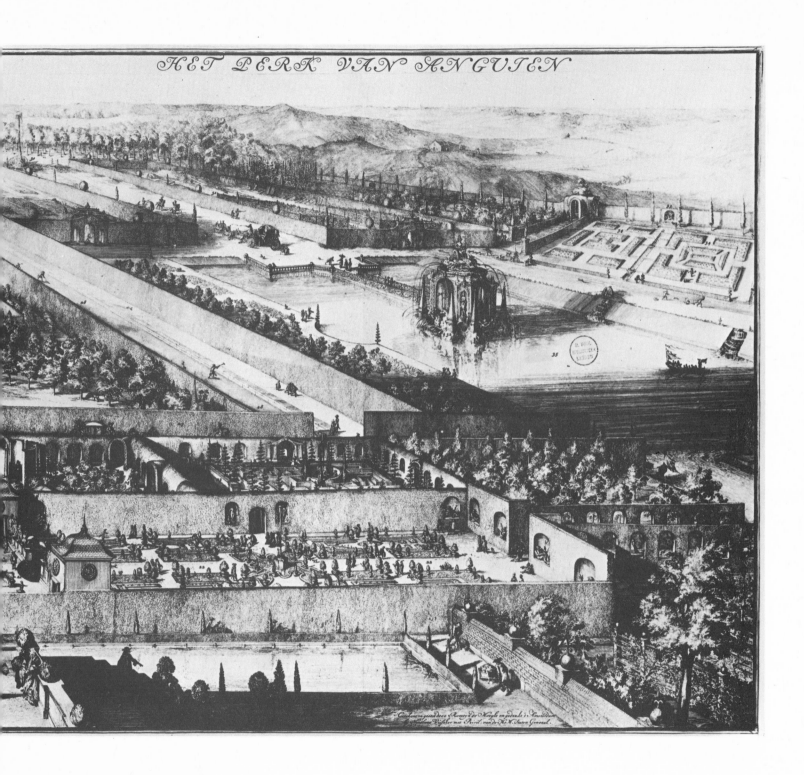

HET PERK VAN ANGUIEN

Geteekent en Geetst door Romeyn de Hooghe, Amst.
N. Visscher

317

VILLA ANGIANA,

Vulgo

HET PERC VAN

ANGUIEN

Serenisfimo Principi,

D: D: PHILIPPO CAROLO, Dei Gratia Duci Arembergio, Arschotio, de Crouy etc:
hæc non tantum Belgii, Sed totius EUROPÆ TEMPE, ut Sua Seq, ipsum devorit
Nicolaus Visscher. Amst: Bat: qui Suis Sumptibus hæc primo in lucem edidit cum Privil: Ordin: General: Belgii Fœderati.

H275-285 Romanus de Hooghe Delin et Sculp. each print   c. 22.3 × 28.3 cm
With pamphlet of 14 pages (last page with *impressum* of N. Visscher)

318

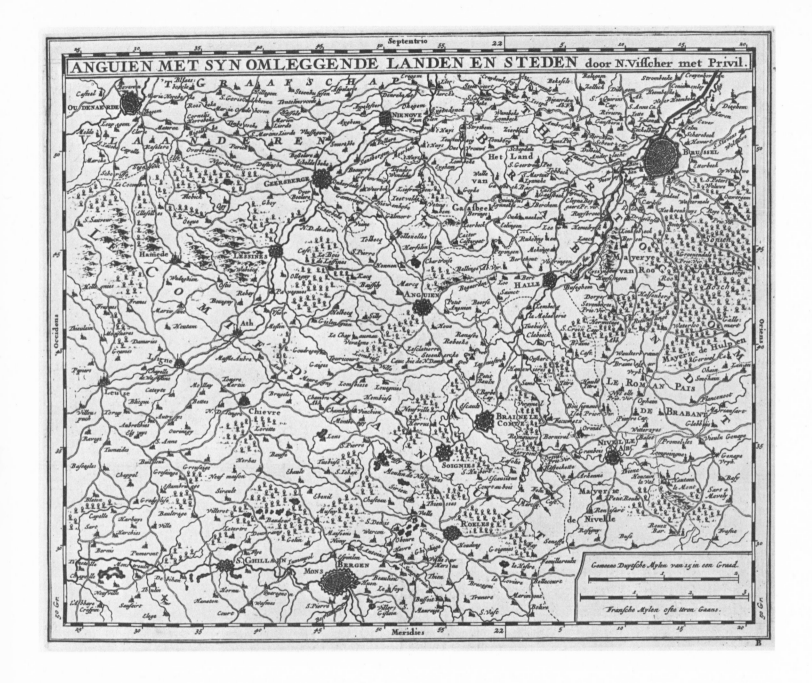

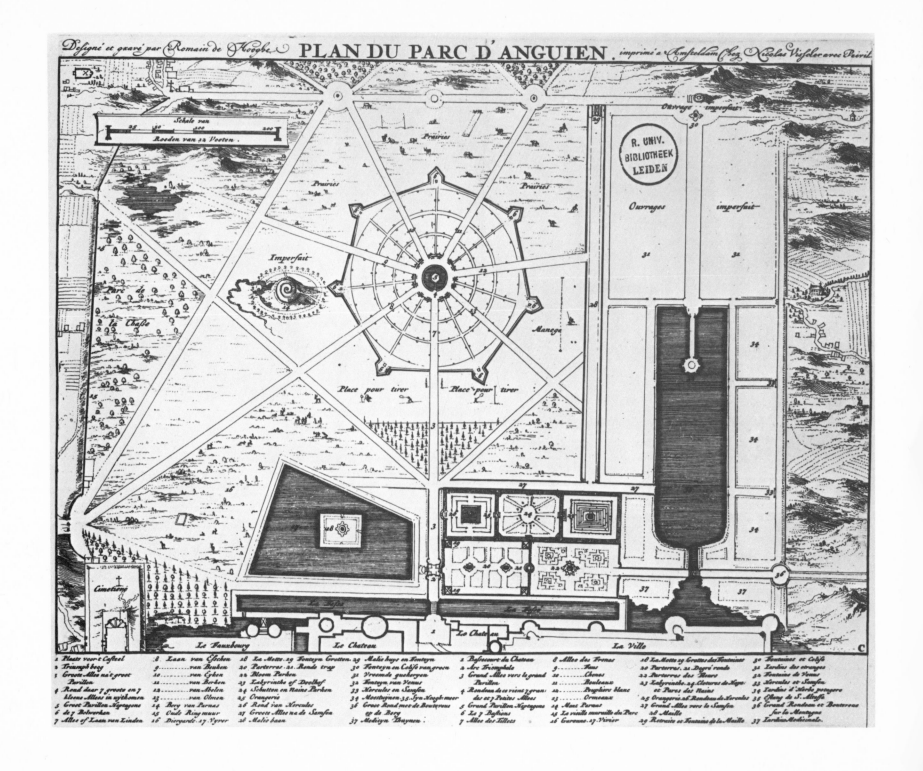

ANNO 1685

Designé et gravé par Romain de Hooghe.

2. Triumph-Boog oft Poort van 't Parc.

2. l'Arc triumphale ou Porte du Parc.   D

3. Groote Alleé oft groene laan na 't groote Pavilloen.

3. Grand alleé vers le grand Pavillon.

5. 't Groot Pavillioen.   18. la Motte.

5. le Grand Pavillon.   18. la Motte.

a Amstellam chez Nicolas Visscher avec Privil: des Estats Generals.

321

4. Rond daer 7 groote en 7 kleene alleés op uytkomen. 5. t Groot Pavilloen.
9. Alleé of Laan van Beukeboomen. 10. Alleé of Laan van Eykeboomen.
11. Laan van Berkeboomen. 12. Laan van Abeleboomen.

4. Rondeau de ce vient 7 grandes et 7 petites Alleés.
5. le Grand Pavillon. 9. Alleé des Faus. 10. Alleé des Chenes.
11. Alleé des Bouleaux. 12. Alleé des Peupliers blanc.

a Amstetdam chez Nicolas Vischer avec Privil. des Estats Generals.

E

grove par Romain de Hooghe

4. Rond daar 7 groote en 7 kleene Allees op uytkomen.   4. Rondeau de ce vient 7 grandes et 7 petites Allees.   F

5. 't Groot Pavillioen.   8. Allee of Laan van Esseboomen.   5. le Grand Pavillon.   8. Allee des Frenes.

12. Allee of Laan van Abeleboomen.   13. Olmeboomen.   12. Allee des Peupliers blanc.   13. Allee des Ormeaux.

a Amsteldam chez Nicolas Visscher avec Privil. des Estatz Generals.

6. Een der 7 Bolwerken die tegen de kleene groene Alleés
   oft Lanen responderen.
14. Berg van Parnas. 15 Oude ringmuur van 't perk.

6. Un des 7 Bastions qui respondent au petits Alleés.
14. Mont Parnas.
15. la Vieille muraille du Parc.

a Amstollam chez Nicolas Visscher avec Privil. des Estats Generals

Defigné et gravé par Romain de Hooghe.

2. Triumph-boog oft Poort van 't Perk.
15. d'Oude ringmuur van 't Perk.
16. Diergaerde............ 17. de Vyver............ 18. la Motte.

2. l'Arc Triomphale ou Porte du Parc.
15. la Vielle muraille du Parc. 16. Garonne.
17. le Vivier.............................. 18. la Motte.

H

a Amsteldam chez Nicolas Visscher avec Privil. des Estats Generals

2. *Triumphboog of Poort van 't Perk.*
18. *la Motte*............. 19. *Fonteyngrotten.*
20. *Parterres of Cierperken van Palm.*

2. *l'Arc Triomphale ou Porte du Parc.*
18. *la Motte*........... 19. *Grottes des Fontaines.*
20. *Parterres des Fleurons.*

.I

a Amsterdam chez Nicolas Visscher avec Privil. des Estats Generals.

2. Triumph-boog oft Poort van 't Perk.

19. Fonteyngrotten .... 21. Groote ronde trap.

22. Bloemhof en Bloemperken.

2. l'Arc Triomphale ou Porte du Parc.

19. Grottes des Fontaines ...... 21. Degré ronde.

22. Parterres des Fleurs.

K.

a Amsterdam chez Nicolas Visscher avec Privil. des Estats Generals.

23. *Het Labyrinthe oft Doolhof met de schoone Fonteyn van Amphitrite.*

23. *le Labyrinthe avec la magnifique Fontaine d'Amphitrite.*

I.

a Amsterdam chez Nicolas Visscher avec Privil. des Estats Generals.

Designé et gravé par Romein de Hooghe.

24. Rondt met groene schutten en perken met naintjes oft dwergboomtjes.

24. Rondeau avec clotures de haye et parcs des nains.

M

a Amsterdam chez Nicolas Visscher avec Privil. des Estats Generals.

Defigné et gravé par Romain de Hooghe.

25. Orangien Hoff met de marmere Fonteyn van de drie Gratien.

26. Rond van Hercules met twee termen aan de fyden.

25. Orangerie avec la Fontaine marbre de trois Graces.

26. Rondeau de Hercule avec deux termes.

t Amfteldam chez Nicolas Viffcher avec Privil. des Eftats Generals.

Dessiné et gravé par Romain de Hooghe.

27. Groote Alleé oft Laan na de Samson. 28. de Maliebaan .

29. Maliehuys en Fonteyn .... 33. Pavillioen van Samson .

34. Moesthuynen........................ 35. 't Meer van syn Hoogheyt.

27. Grande Alleé vers le Pavillon de Samson 28. le Maille . O

29. Retraite et Fontaine du Maille . 33. Pavillon de Samson .

34. Jardins d'herbe potagere.........35. Estang de son Altesse .

à Amsteldam chez Nicolas Visscher avec Privil. des Estats Generals.

30. *Fonteyn en Colise van groente.*   30. *Fontaine et Colise de Verdure.*   P

a Amsteldam chez Nicolas Visscher avec Privil. des Estats Generals.

Desseigné et gravé par Romain de Hooghe.

32. Een gedeelte van de Fonteyn van Venus.   32. Une partie de la Fontaine de Venus.

33. Pavillioen van Samson. 34. Moesthuynen.   33. Pavillon de Samson. 34. Jardins d'herbe potagere.

35. Het Meer van syn Hoogheyt.   35. Estang de son Altesse.

a Amsteldam chez Nicolas Visscher avec Privil. des Estats Generals.

Desiné et gravé par Romain de Hooghe.

34. *Moesthuynen.*
36. *Groot rond met de bouteveue op den berg.*
37. *Medecynthuynen.*

34. *les Jardins d'herbe potagere.*
36. *Grand rondeau avec le bouteveue sur la montagne.*
37. *les Jardins medicinals.*

R

a Amsteldam chez Nicolas Visscher avec Privil. des Estats Generals.

R. d. Hooge fe. J. Tangena ex cum privilegio

H286 R. d. Hooge fe. J. Tangena ex...
13 × 48 cm

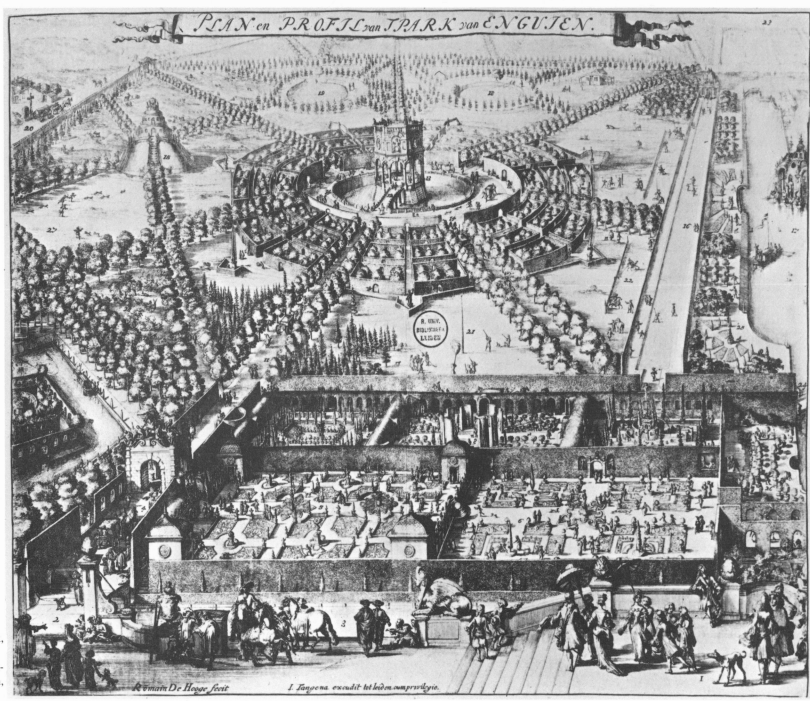

PLAN en PROFIL van 'T PARK van ENGUIEN.

Romain De Hooge fecit   I. Tangena. excudit tot leiden.cum privilegie.

Leyden University Library. Romain De Hooge fecit,
J. Tangena excudit tot leiden   38 × 46.5 cm
With pamphlet of 6 pages „Plate Grond ... van het onweergadelijke Lust-perk van ENGUIEN ... Tot Leyden,
by Johannes Tangena

H288-300 signed Romeyn de Hooghe … dedicated to the City Council   c. 173 × 200 cm
The twelve insets were also used in Th. Schrevelius' *Harlemias* 1750
…*Beautifully situated compared to all the other places, provided with dunes rich in hunting opportunities, rivers abounding in fish, the best soil one could wish for gardens*…

vSt supp. FM2990 H200 (= 302) dedication by de Hooghe, no address   50 × 57.5 cm
…Knowledge and reading, up to the learning of languages only taught at the universities, is so general here that many women also seem to want to be acquainted with Latin, Greek or Hebrew…

LISBONA

Rijksmuseum Amsterdam. H303 not signed, no address
14.5 × 18.5 cm

HET LOO AND ITS PARK

A bird's eye view with the inscription 'T KONINGSLOO, and a set of fourteen etchings including a profile. The old castle was acquired by Willem III in 1686 and then he built Het Loo; for its park De Hooghe designed statues representing river gods; the set of drawings is reproduced by kind permission of Atlas van Stolk, Rotterdam

Lit.: A. G. Bienfait. *Oud Hollandsche Tuinen*. The Hague 1943. pp. 90ff.
Nederlandsche Spectator, 1875 p. 348 *ff.*

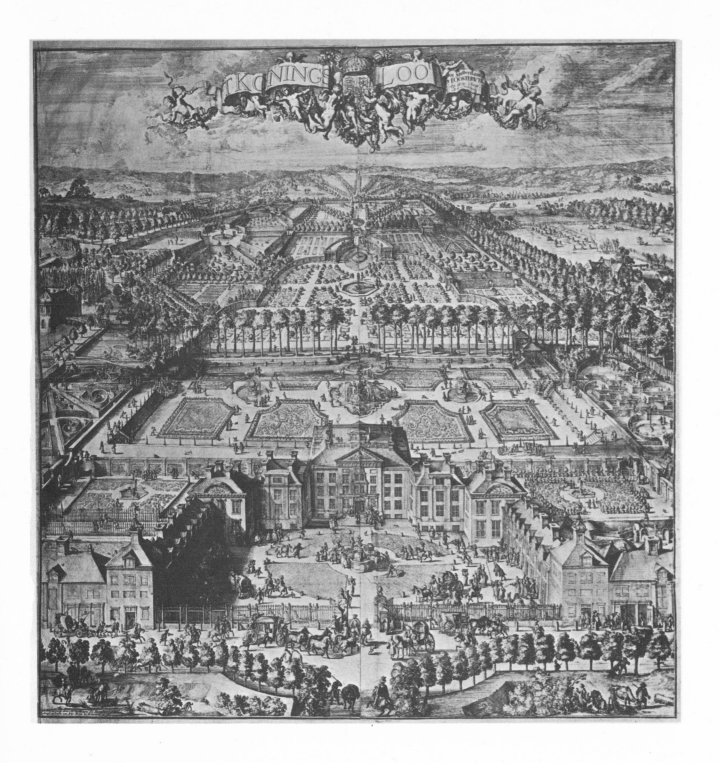

I : Romeyn de Hooghe, address (top and below) Pieter
Persoy. 4 plates   37.7 × 36.6 cm
II: vSt2719 H307 Romeyn de Hooghe, address (top)
J. Oosterwijk

I : H304-306 Getekend en geëtst door Mr. Romeyn de
    Hooghe, address P. Persoy Amst.   c. 18 × 120 cm
II: without address in: *Korte beschrijving … van 't Loo* –
    see LA 109
*…The Veluwe is an island cut off from the land by the
Rhine, the Vecht, the Yssel and the Zuyder Zee; it is
wooded, full of large ditches, mills, parks and it is also
famous for King's Loo, the grand and magnificent
hunting-lodge belonging to the great William of Nassau,
King of Great Britain…*

HET LOO – THE OLD CASTLE

HET OUD CASTEEL
Figuur 1.

1 de Aeer-sprong. 2 Weg na 't groot Baffin. 3 Bosch en thuyn van't eud Casteel. 4. Allee na de Heeren weg voor 4 Hof verbygaende. 5 de Vleugels van't Hof.   *Rom. de Hooge delin: et sculp:*

I : H309 Rom. de Hooge delin: et sculp:,
   address P. Persoy, Amst.   c. 19 × 25 cm
II: without address in: *Korte beschrijving ... van 't Loo* –
   see LA 109

343

HET LOO

I : H321 address P. Persoy, Amst.   c. 19 × 25 cm
II: without address in: *Korte beschrijving… van 't Loo* –
    see LA 109

355

Series of eight designs of statues. each
c. 30 × 52 cm
Atlas van Stolk, Rotterdam

357

358

359

De Najads of Nymphs van Zoo
met swaerze sied Cinzel get gekronckelde leeden
hare darhve sweeren, in d' hemden, redo chenhelende
by hadt hayeten is een guirlands van blaederen tusse
grof boom loof gesneghe breit, recht midden van dese
wpre't een vroon toorn het geboun, het hemedt
het hoit om de hoogte, in schragen van hade wate
door siere hare kinyk to de schrod de wate
van de wate val achte lant hade sierlych heiri
loopt om sig met den yset to schenigin de hade
leschooft om de rijedom di ofte van her na brye sie
ontfanght by heht hoit den sidny, in sijn seut haet
de schoelykigny van sijn vloe st ahe dat sijn
waterwas, t himmut wat sy hehte d' nissthe
sijn hooft is van freis aet, sehen bladen ihe hedist
sijn schne rad staet aght hem van d' wat irmulits
dives het gaet, to geta is afgades berg aghty
wat op hety in strenallen to sonsyn.

361

De Vorst

Staat in de gedachte van Apollo die
als de sou, aen alles het uselvaeren, en de
waedom geesst, en so het sieraaden en de
docht, de waabl godinge weten. Soo
als de goo van de saelt komt hij bij
sijn suft geordschap, godomet Hooleen de
het Vijtlisch ongedient, schiudt de ou van
duerelijt, de woorschiydt van de Heij
de Nympsi schenckt hem de oudelaste
die sou en sijn te Hoochgyt ontsangen
heeft met drou, hij is gedacht met
ben Kostelijkraad, ne ith gedrivt of hij
geseten, Haer Lockden, sninden nychlijk
near Hair Bosform, de hegter Haer voen
vallende als Hadis wat he livijns knop
de Sirievelen in waat van sa de waadu
lijks dovt gaan, de rest van Handewerr
sluyr, se een ladsh na den Ijel.

ARX ET OPPIDUM
MONTISMELIANI.

H328a (?) Romanus de Hooghe exaravit A° 1675
46.5 × 58 cm
in *Theatrum Statuum Regiae Celsitudinis Sabaudiae*
Ducis, Pedemonti Principis, Cypri Regis. Amsterdam,
J. Blaeu 1682

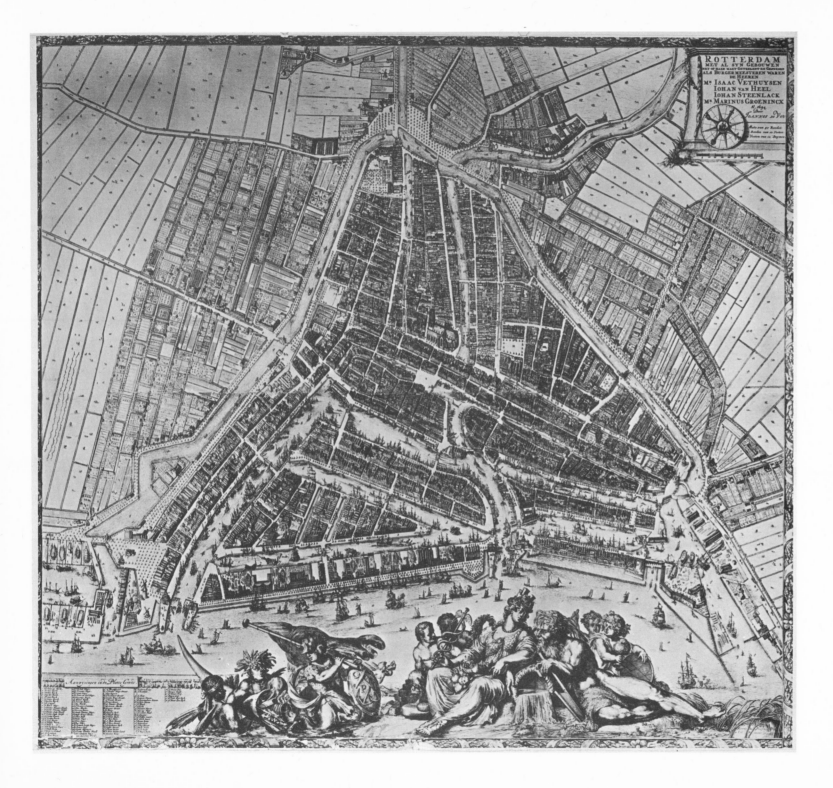

H328b not signed   175 × 225 cm
Plan partly reproduced with *vignettes* by De Hooghe, with border on top of coats of arms, six views at right and left sides namely: Het Stadt-Huys, Laurens Kerck, De Franse Kerck, De Prinse Kerck, De Beurse, De Marckt, De Vismarkt, De Doelen, 't Gemeenelandts Huys van Schielandt, 't Admiraliteytshof, 't Nieuw Hooft, 't Oude Hooft (all signed: „D. Vou f.")
Below large view ROTTERDAMUM – prospect of the Meuse.

Lit: A. C. de Neve. *De Kaart van de Vou,* in: Nieuwe Rotterdamsche Courant, 30 December 1939.
– B. van 't Hoff. *„De Plattegronden van de stad Rotterdam in de 16de en 17de eeuw,* in: Het Boek xxx, pp. 63-64
Facsimile: fa. Langerveld Rotterdam 1968

SALZDAHLEM (near Brunswick, Germany)

Teyler Museum Haarlem. H329-331 Romano de Hooghe
Comm. R. Auct. (three leaves)   96 × 68.5 cm

366

PLATEAE VETERIS

PROSPE...US   ANTE   CASTRVM

H333 (?) R. de Hooghe f in *Theatrum Statuum Regiae Celsitudinis Sabaudiae Ducis...* Apud Haeredes Joannes Blaeu MDCLXXII   45.5 × 61 cm

H333 not signed, no address   c. 46.5 × 58.5 cm

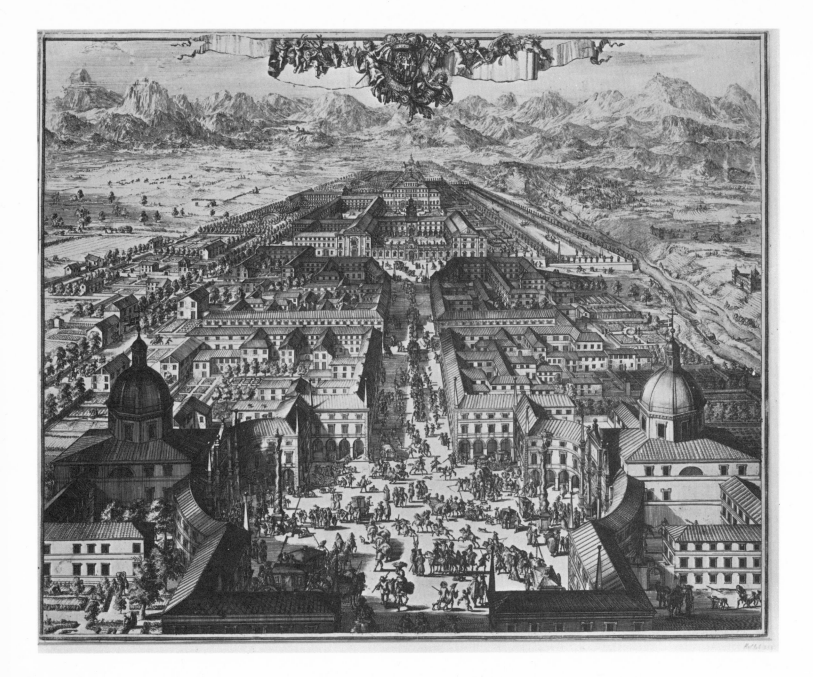

H333 not signed, no address   c. 47 × 59.5 cm

MORALS AND CUSTOMS

CAPRICCI – four prints

FIGURES A LA MODE – twelve prints

References: H   F. W. H. Hollstein. *Dutch and Flemish Etchings. Engravings and Woodcuts.*

Volume IX. Amsterdam 1953

FM   F. Muller. *De Nederlandsche geschiedenis in platen.*

Amsterdam 1863-1882. 4 vols. (Reprint: Amsterdam 1970)

vSt   G. van Rijn. *Atlas van Stolk.*

Amsterdam, 's-Gravenhage 1895-1931. 10 vols. *Index.* 's-Gravenhage 1933

H359 R. de Hooge, address N. Visscher   16.1 × 11.8 cm

...The women are diligent, tidy in their housekeeping, far too good to the children...

CAPRICCI

H360 not signed   16.1 × 11.8 cm

...Men and woman still compare favourably with the neighbouring peoples as to modesty...

H361 not signed   16 × 11.8 cm

...although the good morals (God forbid!) gradually become somewhat scarcer and deteriorated through love of ease and prosperity...

H362 not signed   16.2 × 11.8 cm

...often the good morals are badly influenced by the frivolity of foreigners...

Figures a
la mode
inventez et gravez
par
R: de Hooge
et mis en lumiere
par N: Visscher.

H363 R: de Hooge, N. Visscher (Amst.)   16 × 11.6 cm
a self-portrait?

H364 not signed   16.1 × 11.7 cm

*...It cannot be denied... that in the towns all kinds of
cloths and materials (are found)...*

H365 not signed   16.1 × 11.8 cm

…all the materials and yarns are pre-eminently improved in quality as well in fineness as in lightness…

H366 not signed   16 × 11.7 cm

...ever so elegant from the outside and everything sewn
very neatly, expensive materials as well...

H367 not signed   16 × 11.6 cm

…or so lightly for the less expensive materials that foreigners simply have to buy them…

H368 not signed   16 × 11.7 cm

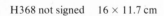

...the same applies to clothes, for it is easy to see whether
the burghers carry on trade close to the courts...

7

H369 not signed   16 × 11.6 cm

…(whether the burghers carry on trade) amongst noblemen or warriors…

H370 not signed   16 × 11.6 cm

…or whether they associate with merchants and then dress
less elegantly and courtly…

H371 not signed   16 × 11.6 cm

…Does that man appear to be so powerful?…

H372 not signed   16.1 × 11.8 cm

...Politeness has already been more or less generally adopted by young and old...

H373 not signed   16 × 11.6 cm

...something of the old Dutch and Frisian and also of the austere attire of the Mennonites contributes to modesty in fashion...

H374 not signed   16 × 11.6 cm

...wives who have cupboards crammed with the finest linen...

ALLEGORIES

The complicate marriage in Nijmegen 1618

Allegory on the thesis of F. W. Schmitz

Allegory dedicated to the Duke of Toscane

Allegory dedicated to Baronet of Schagen

The election of Karl Heinrich Archbishop of Mainz

References: H   F. W. H. Hollstein. *Dutch and Flemish Etchings. Engravings and Woodcuts.*

Volume IX. Amsterdam 1953

FM   F. Muller. *De Nederlandsche geschiedenis in platen.*

Amsterdam 1863-1882. 4 vols. (Reprint: Amsterdam 1970)

vSt   G. van Rijn. *Atlas van Stolk.*

Amsterdam, 's-Gravenhage 1895-1931. 10 vols. *Index.* 's-Gravenhage 1933

De Vrouw spreekt.

Dees prent verbeelt u Man en Vrouw
In Egt verbonden door de Trouw:
De outste Jongmans beydegader
Dat syn twee broeders van mijn Vader:

De Jongmans aan mijn linker hant
Zijn Oomen van mijn Moeders kant:
De Kinders die hier voor my speelen
Die quam ik by mijn Man te teelen;

Ook maakt den Egt my Moeder van
Mijn Oomen, Zonen van mijn Man;
Die my ook, (volgens Godts begeeren)
Als Nigt en Moeder moeten eeren.
P. van TORENBURG.

Zes zonen, hier gemaalt, zyn 't kroost vand'oude Man
Die neerzit by zyn Vrouw, de Nigte en Moeder van

De vier en twé; dus noemt tot zes toe elk een broeder
Vier broeders van de twé zyn Omen van de Moeder.
SAMUEL SYLVIUS. 1698

I : vSt supp. FM1418A, 3011 and supp. H201 A° 1698
    R. de Hooge fecit, no address   26 × 34.5 cm
II : vSt1455 FM3011 Aa. Poem with six and four lines.
    Address: Nijmegen, Abr. van Wesel 1698
III: vSt1456 FM3011 Ac. Quatrain by Silvius and poem
    of 14 lines. Address: G. de Broen Amst.
IV: vSt1457 FM3011 Ab. One six line poem and two
    quatrains engraved in the plate, not signed.
V : FM3011 C. not signed, address: Nijmegen Is. van
    Campen 1777.
    Lit. Navorscher IV, 273

Teyler Museum Haarlem. Romanus de Hooghe inv.: et
fec. Amstelod.   50.5 × 39 cm

Dedicace au Duc de Toscane

ALLEGORY DEDICATED TO THE DUKE OF
TOSCANE (?)

Albertina Vienna Romano de Hooghe Amstelodamus
1682 Auct. et. (?), no address   37 × 26.5 cm

395

ALLEGORY DEDICATED TO BARONET OF
SCHAGEN

Albertina Vienna not signed, no address   c. 50 × 64 cm

I   : H45 before the letter   50.5 × 37 cm
      Also in: N. Person *Novae Archepiscopatus Moguntini*
      Tabulae (Mainz, no date)
II : v. Stolk, only with signature: Romanus de Hooghe
      inv. et. f. Amstelodami
III: Teyler Museum Haarlem, as reproduced

Colophon

The present edition of Romeyn de Hooghe The Etcher
by John Landwehr, is set in Times,
printed November 1972 by Verenigde Offset-Bedrijven B.V., Hardenberg,
on paper supplied by M. Ubbens Papiergroothandel, Zutphen,
and bound by Samsom-Sijthoff, Alphen/Leiden
in 1000 numbered copies.
Book Design by W. H. Tweehuysen, Loridan N.V., Leiden.

This copy is number 198